Reasons And Remedies

Reasons And Remedies

Patricia Sims

Mortimore Books

Copyright © Patricia Sims 2000
First published in 2000 by Mortimore Books
Reprinted in 2001
Second edition 2002

The right of Patricia Sims to be identified as the author of this work has been asserted in accordance with the Copyright, Designs and Patents Act 1988.

A catalogue record for this book is available from the British Library

ISBN 0 9536209 2 1

Mortimore Books, PO Box 156, Barnstaple, Devon, EX33 1YN

Printed and bound in Great Britain by
The Bath Press, Bath

Cover design by James Bonetta

CONTENTS

ALSO BY PATRICIA SIMS

Personality Checklist
ISBN 0 9536209 1 3 Published by Mortimore Books

This is a reproducible A4 version of the Personality Checklist from Reasons and Remedies. It provides ample space for written comments.

AUTHOR'S NOTE

In the many places where 'he' or 'she' has been intended I have written 'he' partly to avoid awkwardness of expression, and partly because there are many more boys than there are girls with learning difficulties.

Some details have been altered in case studies to protect children's identities but care has been taken to make such changes as would not distort essential facts or invalidate any claims made.

ACKNOWLEDGEMENTS

My thanks are due to Pamela Bradley, Peter Hames, Ian Lewin, Carol North, and my husband Derek for their helpful comments and I am also grateful to Tilly Marshall and Carol North for allowing me to quote from their own books.

I thank the many children and parents who have passed through my clinics and particularly those parents who suggested that such a book be written.

And thank you Louise Langabeer.

FOREWORD

The need for children's services to work together has long been recognised. Sometimes the call is for multi-disciplinary collaboration, or inter-agency work, and more grandly – seamless services. All of the helping professions that support children with difficulties agree that there is a genuine need to work more closely together. We need to develop a shared language. Our theories and concepts serve more to separate us, even though the practical techniques and strategies have much in common.

At one level *Reasons and Remedies* can be read to better understand the many difficulties that children face. Patricia gives wide coverage to those that she has observed in her clinical practice. Her emphasis on "switching off and avoidance behaviour" is presented to show that, at the heart of many difficulties a clinician may face in helping children, are these coping strategies, which we need to understand. Practical suggestions are then provided.

Patricia's next contribution is to link personality traits with the manner in which children perform in a wide range of settings. Through practice she came to realise that children's milestones alone are of little use, unless you know the child. And to know the child is to take a much more holistic approach through understanding their individual temperament. The key block that exists, often unrecognised in Patricia's view, is anxiety. This pervades many difficulties and becomes the emotional barrier to a child being able to risk going forward.

The rich and creative use of case studies serves to emphasise the need to link both temperament and behavioural categories. It is creative because we explore the minds of such people as Florence Nightingale and L.S. Lowry to explore autism for example. While the book seeks to raise understanding, it is written by a practitioner whose aim is to go beyond theory and present a reality that fellow practitioners and parents can use.

To return to my earlier point of the need for professionals to work closer together: Patricia is a speech and language therapist; she has met childhood emotional and behavioural difficulties similar to those frequently referred by parents to GP's, or by schools to educational psychologists. The diagnostic label and support children and their families receive is as much linked to the professional who sees them, as to the nature of their difficulties. It is therefore refreshing and challenging to see a fellow professional write so compellingly and insightfully about issues that many consider to be their prerogative only. As Patricia says, "if there is an understanding of the person there is also an understanding of his difficulties" and this book shows a fellow practitioner's journey towards this goal.

Rob Long, Educational Psychologist

COMMENTS ON REASONS AND REMEDIES

'I found *Reasons and Remedies* totally absorbing. I identified with it all the way through and I have *LEARNT*! I thought I knew ADHD back to front, but it has filled in many 'missing pieces' from the puzzle.

Yes! Tension and anxiety rule in the homes of ADHD, autistic children, the born worriers, etc. This is the missing link! How imperative is the study of personality traits!

It is a breakthrough in the prevention of mental health problems, alcoholism, crime, drug-taking, suicide and family breakdown.

It has been staring us in the face!

This book brings home the vital importance of training for professionals such as teachers, social workers, child guidance clinicians and behaviour modifiers.

It gives a real, true insight into problems that cause immense emotional and often destructive pain to families.'

Gill Mead, President, ADD/ADHD Family Support Group UK

'This refreshing book is full of insights into a whole range of special needs. I wish I had had it 20 years ago!'

Edwina Cooper, Special Needs Teacher

'A very enthusiastic and personal book. Easy to read, it should stimulate creative thought, however experienced the reader.'

Speech & Language Therapy in Practice

'Reasons and Remedies is an absorbing book... would welcome further analysis of epilepsy in this context.'

The National Society for Epilepsy

'This book gives a refreshing and holistic insight into how to help children struggling with communication skills... gives an insight into the behaviour of children with a wide range of learning disabilities, and should increase understanding and improve services. It should be useful to anybody involved with such children, especially their parents.'

Journal of the Community Practitioners' & Health Visitors' Association

'The whole book is grounded in practicalities that make it accessible to parents as well as professionals.'

REACH (National Advice Centre for Children with Reading Difficulties)

'I found the checklist at the back to be particularly useful.'

Association of Speech and Language Therapists in Independent Practice

'Brilliant in every way! And so readable! My wish is that anyone and everyone who comes into contact with children would read it – it's a must!'

Val Bleasdale, Parent

CHAPTER ONE

INTRODUCTION

"I shall never do this job again full-time" I announced to my husband. *"Not even when we've got grown up children."* It was the early seventies. I was a young speech and language therapist who had finished her demanding university training a year or two previously, and I had had a typical day.

What was one expected to do with a child who refuses to talk, another who spends the session sitting under the table and a third who runs riot around the room? By lunch times I frequently had a bout of indigestion and once or twice, whilst advising voice patients that their aching throats were related to tension, I found myself in the ironical situation of suffering the symptoms I was trying to cure. I knew that I deserved my pay because I regularly went to hell and back with a smile on my face yet I was not convinced that I had entirely earned it. I envied the postman who could take birthday cards to children; I seemed often to be giving them things they did not want.

Some youngsters of course were not at all difficult. They responded well, sometimes enthusiastically, to therapy, and they and their parents were my ego boosters. These children tended to be the older ones – perhaps already five or more years of age – who were ready to change their speech and could benefit from help and encouragement. But they were now in a minority. The trend towards earlier referral of children to speech and language clinics was causing an increase of enigmatic preschool children in case loads.

I no longer have the problems to which I have been referring. My working day has been transformed and my job satisfaction has soared. This is not due to experience which comes with age but to a different method of working which has given me new insight and enabled me not only to properly understand the children but also to have a better appreciation of their difficulties and why these have come about.

Speech, language, learning and social problems, such as stammering, dyslexia and autism, need no longer be puzzling. If we enquire in some depth into the personality traits of young children, we will discover mechanisms which lie behind such problems. We limit our understanding because we adhere to erroneous assumptions and because we have a tendency to ignore, and believe we understand, that which is commonplace.

COMPARING APPROACHES

How shall we treat Matt?

Let us invent a little boy and call him Matt. He is typical of many children who are referred for speech and language therapy. He is aged three years and three months. His parents and health visitor are concerned because he rarely puts more than two or three words together, except when speaking gibberish, and he does not always seem to understand. He has passed a screening test of hearing.

1. A Traditional Approach

A case history is taken. It transpires that Matt babbled normally, said one or two words when one year old but then his speech failed to make good progress. He did not begin to put two words together until he was past two and a half; his vocabulary consists of no more than twenty or so words. He often ignores people and has always done so. His elder brother had some speech difficulties although his sister was forward in everything.

Matt's mother's pregnancy was normal, as was his birth. He sat at an appropriate time, shuffled around on his bottom instead of crawling and finally walked at sixteen months. He was toilet trained at an appropriate time.

Matt was a very quiet, good baby but he now has frequent temper tantrums. He attends a playgroup where his play is deemed satisfactory, although he is somewhat reticent.

General health and physical co-ordination appear satisfactory.

Some Possible Actions, Outcomes and Conclusions:

Matt is encouraged to name some pictures but does not co-operate. He does co-operate to a degree with the first few items of a toy-based test of verbal comprehension but refuses to proceed once the instructions become slightly more complex; he scores a year below his chronological age.

Matt's mother is advised on how to encourage better speech, listening and comprehension from her son, but this is perhaps done somewhat tentatively, since she has already raised her daughter Bee who excels in these areas. (She has blamed Bee for doing all Matt's speaking for him.) Matt displays no interest in pictures which are drawn in a book to help his auditory discrimination between sounds – it is hoped that he will show more enthusiasm for them at home.

Matt's health visitor and general practitioner are informed of his short-comings but no reasons for them are offered. It will be assumed that he is just a bit 'slow' in some areas – "a lot of boys are." Therapy will be attempted but it is felt that Matt may be too immature to respond well to it.

2. An Holistic Approach

I extend the case history to include a range of questions which lead to insight, for both therapist and parent, into a child's personality traits.

Matt is happy during the session. He is busy playing with toys but he listens in on my conversation with his mother. He finds it rather reassuring to have his little fears and habits aired and his mother seems to be enjoying the chat. These adults appear to understand not only him, but lots of other children who behave the same as him. When he first entered the room Matt had eyed me with suspicion, but since I have not made any demands on him and do not appear critical, he comes up to me from time to time to ask for something or to give me tea from the toy tea-set. He is obviously more likely to respond to any test procedures, should they be considered necessary later on. His mother says she is amazed at his response. She had not expected him to talk at all; he had not wanted to come and had made a scene about it. She also tells me that the session has been invaluable to her.

What might we have learned about Matt that we are unlikely to have discovered taking a more traditional approach? Perhaps one of his traits proves to be a certain fussiness for his age, with him putting away his toys, each in its own proper place, after playing with them, and we may have seen a relevance in his dislike of being wet or dirty or in his fussiness over food. We might have discussed a great sensitivity to criticism, some avoidance and independence, a liking for sameness, order, ritual and repetition, and his fears and bed-wetting.

It no longer perplexes Matt's mother that his speech has been slow to develop. The delay in speech fits in with his general behaviour. He wishes to keep the status quo and make changes gradually as his motivation to change overrides his reticence, or when his confidence has grown sufficiently. We link his repetitive speech, gibberish and liking for particular words to his tension and need for sameness. We understand that there will be some reluctance to break familiar patterns of behaviour and speak in more grown-up sentences. We can appreciate why he might not always listen and why he may need things to be explained very precisely and unambiguously. We can see that getting excited when he says a new word clearly, praising him for it and asking him for a repeat performance might well have an inhibiting effect, by drawing his attention to the change.

We discuss the fact that Matt is a normal little boy and that anxiety or tension is normal and essential to us all – but that the manner in which we express it can make us appear slow or lazy. Matt's mother can see that pressurising him to talk will be counterproductive but that a conversation with her husband, health visitor, the playgroup leader, and of course Matt himself, might help to remove or lessen any environmental factors which could be helping to raise levels of anxiety or tension. We begin to note all the positive signs of change in Matt. His mother is relieved that he is not a 'slow' child and she is no longer likely to compare his development with that of the girl down the road. Alert to his sensitivity and not misconstruing his actions, she is more likely to respond appropriately.

It may be that Matt's case will involve no further intervention; possibly a little support will be all that is called for. Any action taken will be based on an improved understanding of the child's feelings and behaviour.

A NEED FOR CHANGE

In these days of abundant and sometimes excessive change it seems unfortunate that we remain entrenched in the manner in which we view children. Since we do not look carefully enough at what their personality traits are telling us, we fail to have a proper understanding of their problems. Our equipment for testing our children's ability grows in quantity and sophistication whilst our knowledge of why they perform as they do has remained limited. This in turn restricts the help we offer and may result in us taking inappropriate action.

Unless investigative procedures of the type detailed in this book are followed, I do not think it is possible to have a proper understanding of conditions such as dyslexia, general learning difficulties, autism, stammering and other speech and language difficulties, epilepsy, Tourette syndrome, Attention Deficit Hyperactivity Disorder, dyspraxia, social or conduct disorders and mental illness.

The Current Situation

As a group, professionals working with children must surely be among the most hard-working, caring and dedicated people in our society. But is their time put to best use? Many of us take case histories, carry out tests, and then offer advice or set to work trying to teach the child whatever it is that he cannot do. If our methods do not produce favourable results we have a tendency to blame the child's immaturity, his difficult behaviour, his dys-praxia, his parent's poor co-operation, or some other convenient factor. But have we based our advice or treatment on firm foundations? Have we really found out everything we need to know about the child and have we properly understood whatever we have discovered? It is my conviction that there are worldwide shortcomings in these areas and that these need to be addressed by the use of a more holistic approach.

Many of us who have children think that we understand them and their personalities. Some of us may do. Others admit to being at a loss, and despair. Some more of us, in fear or in optimism, fail to acknowledge possible problems or we believe the youngsters will, with time and correction, conform to our requirements. Were we to closely observe and sensitively examine our child's behaviour we could save him, ourselves and others pain and disappointment and he would benefit enormously from knowing that we love and accept him for who he is, not for what he is going to become.

Each child is highly individual. A label can be useful in acquiring educational help or achieving acceptance of a condition, but we should be wary, since it also tends to make us think we understand the child because we have given his difficulties a name and have listed some symptoms. It is only by understanding personalities that we will understand those whom we label.

Unfortunately many of us are rather free and careless in the manner in which we describe children so that both we and they come to believe that they really are 'selfish', 'sulky', 'lazy' and so on. Sometimes we ascribe ill-considered but popular reasons to a child's behaviour and stick to them come what may.

Using a Personality Checklist

It was while I was working as a speech and language therapist in a busy clinic that I became aware that normal children, from infancy or early child-hood, display traits in their personalities which give insight into and in some cases govern their performance educationally, socially, artistically and in sport. It became clear to me that these traits are strongly associated with the presence or absence of various levels of anxiety or some kind of tension. I came to realise that even with normal, acceptable anxiety levels, the traits were responsible for a great many of the speech, language and other learning difficulties which I was encountering, problems which occur much more frequently in boys.

I began to change my case history taking. There was little point in merely asking for 'milestones' – when the youngster sat, walked, became toilet trained, etc. – and a certain number of other details involving his health and behaviour, if I did not properly understand why he continued to dribble, why he walked late or why he reacted or behaved as he did. As I began to ask more questions I gained a better understanding of children whom I might formerly have viewed as strange, difficult, dull or even irritating. My enquiries and observations have led me to offer an alternative explanation for some features which are generally considered to be neurological signs, or evidence of brain damage or brain inferiority.

In order to understand children and their problems it is necessary to look in some depth at their personality traits but there is very little point in accumulating information about a child unless the significance of it is appreciated. At the end of this book is a Personality Checklist – a large number of questions, many of which one might need to ask oneself or others with regard to a child. If the contents of the book are carefully considered, answers to the questions will be found to have taken on a new meaning – we shall gain the insight which currently tends to elude us and understand children's problems because we have a fundamental understanding of their behaviour and feelings.

A checklist can be a very helpful tool. During its use, it soon becomes apparent that certain areas of questioning are of relevance to a particular child, and a professional may direct a discussion with a parent accordingly. The better we understand the traits behind the answers, the more fruitful that discussion will be. Then, perhaps with the aid of a further conversation with a health visitor or others, it may be possible for the parent to eliminate or reduce the impact of any environmental factors which provoke or sustain tension or anxious feelings in the child.

Benefits of the Holistic Approach

The benefits which come with the approach I am advocating are comprehensive:

1. For the parent, true understanding brings great relief; his anxiety diminishes, his sympathy and confidence grow and no longer does he take trial and error based steps to help his child.

2. For the child there are huge emotional and performance benefits when he is properly understood.

3. There is greater success and much more job satisfaction for the professional, be he therapist, teacher, educational psychologist, paediatrician, health visitor or from one of the many other disciplines involved with children.

4. For the professional's employer, which is frequently a health or education authority, there is increased efficiency and public satisfaction.

5. For research there are new roads to go down and an increased facility for appreciating the significance of what has already been discovered.

TAKING AN OVERALL VIEW

This book has been written to help both professionals and parents to accurately interpret children's behaviour and hence understand and treat their problems or disabilities – and in some cases to prevent them. It offers an approach which broadens horizons when solutions are sought. It is *not* concerned with classifying and labelling the problems in the first instance, and thence trying to understand the children. The approach enables one to take an overall view of social and learning difficulties and related syndromes, seeing anxiety as a common factor in them, and recognising that they do not exist as entities which are independent of one another. It is hoped that the reader's understanding of a condition will be enhanced by his improved understanding of other ones.

I have endeavoured to highlight the all-important role that tension or anxiety, in a variety of forms or guises and often appearing to be present from birth or early infancy, plays in the development of children. Autism, Asperger's syndrome, dyslexia, hyperactivity, Attention Deficit Hyperactivity Disorder, mental illness, conduct problems, speech and language disorders and Tourette syndrome are included in this book, but any such condition involves a set of traits which are *variable and overlap in an apparently haphazard manner with traits in other conditions.* Whether we call a child autistic, dyslexic, hyperactive or say he is suffering from receptive language problems, specific language impairment (developmental dysphasia) or Tourette syndrome, etc., really depends on his particular traits and the degree to which they are manifest or dominant.

An overall view of social and learning difficulties and their related syndromes is long overdue. Useful research is carried out in the specific areas of autism, dyslexia, speech and language, etc., but a global view of the problems is required, too. Hopefully, we shall also see some comprehensive research carried out into the personality traits of young children.

Much of the significance of this book will be lost if it is not read in sequence. I therefore ask the reader not to select chapters which are felt to have most relevance to him or her. I also ask him to suspend any beliefs that dyslexia, autism, Tourette syndrome, specific language impairment, dyspraxia, stammering and Attention Deficit Hyperactivity Disorder are inherited per se, as entities which are independent of other conditions. I should like to consider the role that personality traits play in forming these conditions.

The next three chapters look at many personality traits which our children exhibit and the ways in which we might interpret them. We shall then be able to see how this holistic approach can be applied to, and help us understand and treat, a range of problems.

CHAPTER TWO

SWITCHING OFF AND AVOIDANCE

SWITCHING OFF

Daydreaming is an international pastime. Psychologists tell us it is a relaxed hypnotic state like the one we are in when we drift off to sleep or awaken each day; it is healthy and perhaps we do not do it enough.

Some children, those we call autistic, do much more than daydream. They are 'switched off' from (or not tuned into) their environment, sometimes to an alarming extent. Whilst the vast majority of children do not show such extreme behaviour, many are switched off in their own way. It is my experience that when switching off leads to problems, there is generally some present or past tension or anxiety associated with it.

Harry

Harry is three. He feels happy and secure at home although he notices that his sister, Alice, who is five, is learning to read and everyone thinks she is really clever. She knows a lot of things. One day Harry goes to playschool for the first time. There are ladies there who tell him to do things. It is exciting but rather strange, too, and he is a little worried. Harry does not listen to the ladies. It is easier to do what he wants. After a year or two, Harry goes to school. Now there is a new lady who is *always* telling him to do things. He has to do what she says but he does not listen. It is easier to copy what the other boys and girls are doing.

After his first eighteen months at school Harry is causing concern. He memorises his reading book but cannot actually read the words. From the start he felt a little panicky, worrying that he might not be able to read them. He could not concentrate and found himself switching off. Even when he succeeds in controlling his responses and does manage to read one or two words properly, he cannot remember them later. Sometimes, when he makes a lot of effort, the words go rather fuzzy. His writing is very poor and he keeps making the same mistakes. And he does not seem to understand at all well. Perhaps he needs spectacles... Harry seems rather 'slow' at the Opticians. He knows he is stupid and he knows Mum and Dad are bothered by his stupidity. Alice has found a good game – "Have a go at this Harry – see if you can do it!" He does not try. He prefers to do something else.

Now Harry is seven. The educational psychologist is coming to see him. He is a nice man but Harry does not do very well at his tests. He switches off regularly – it just seems to happen to him. Whenever he tries to concentrate on what the man is saying or on what he has given him to do, the usual hopeless feelings come over him – and he gives his usual responses.

Rachel

Harry has a slightly anxious personality, although nobody has thought too much about it, but Rachel is very anxious. Her involvement with the external world is restricted for she has become programmed to withhold or withdraw her attention. She soon learned to turn her eyes away from her mother because the expressions on her face seemed painfully involving and alarming. Later she spent her time fiddling with bits of tissue. You could not hold a proper conversation with Rachel but she knew where every cobweb in the house was and she remembered the little mark on Auntie's gate which she had seen a year before. Rachel's responses became programmed during her infancy and few normal feelings and thought patterns were able to compete with them. When she was six, her parents were told that she was autistic.

Harry and Rachel are fictitious, though typical characters whom I have used in two possible scenarios to illustrate the range of the problem of being switched off.

Terms of Reference – Switching Off

I use the term 'switched off' broadly. I intend it to range from a slight or partial absence of attention to a condition where the mind is free of thought. The action might seem to be deliberate or involuntary, habitual, conditioned or even compulsive and the child may be selective in his attention in a consistent way. It sometimes seems that, rather than switching off, a youngster is not engaging his brain or 'tuning in'; he may appear to spend most or all of his time in this state.

Evidence of switching off has been obtained from direct observation, first-hand written and verbal accounts and from accounts of parents and carers.

AVOIDING DEMANDS

I spent a period working as part of a special needs team which, in the main, had dealings with three and four-year-olds who puzzled people. Each of these children had his individual personality and behaved differently, yet all of them switched off or were permanently partially switched off, or they avoided people's demands in some other way; many displayed both types of behaviour.

One little girl who I attempted to assess, quietly turned around in her chair and simply ignored me, whereas another took the test items and gently dropped them on the floor, one after the other. This is obvious avoidance but some little children are more subtle in evading the demands we make on them. One will talk nineteen to the dozen to stop us asking him something or will keep interrupting us; another will pretend to cry – he has a headache, feels sick, tired or unwell. He may be "busy" or will "do it in a minute". He may start giggling or saying the task is boring or silly. He may be downright disruptive. Sometimes we hear, "I don't know" as a reply to almost every-thing asked and the child will pretend to be quite inept, while others will refuse outright with a definite "No!" One little girl was adept at diverting my attention – "Look over there in that corner!" she exclaimed and then suddenly there was something else to look at on the curtain or ceiling. Another child set about rearranging the furniture, apparently to waste time. Some have already learned how to charm their way out of doing things; many employ a diversity of tactics.

It is frequently found that these children speak indistinctly to some de-gree; they may even whisper or refuse to talk at all. They do not always wish to communicate very clearly. Few are encouraged by praise, for praise has been used to cajole them. Indeed, it can be a cue to appear more incapable. One mother told me that whenever she praised her little girl, she would go off to do something naughty.

These youngsters may be 'failing' but they do not lack initiative. As with switching off, their avoidance behaviour can become habitual. Professor Elizabeth Newson at the University of Nottingham's Child Development Research Unit has carried out some interesting work with children who avoid people's demands to a serious degree. She refers to a Pathological Demand Avoidance Syndrome where much or most of the avoidance behav-iour appears to be obsessional. She also draws attention to the children's poor sense of identity and lack of pride, together with surface sociability (Newson, 1989; Newson, 1996). It is my experience that this superficial sociability tends to reassure people that all will be well, so that the true nature of the problem remains undetected and sometimes difficult to accept. It also seems to me that it can hide emotional hypersensitivity and a fear of social situations.

We ought to ask here if these young children, so adept at avoiding, will simply grow out of their habit. Unfortunately, there does not seem to be room for complacency. I have seen older children and youths who still appear to be avoiding in a compulsive way. Alarmingly, one or two of these have succeeded in convincing people, their families included, that they are quite deaf and they are artful enough to lead experienced audiologists a fine dance. Some older girls come to mind who are still giggling and charming their way out of situations which apparently disturb them, yet would seem to most of us benign enough. Leigh, at fourteen, completed a simple task I gave her quickly, efficiently and successfully, but she was quite unable to repeat it. She suddenly displayed utter incompetence, reverting to silly behaviour. A year before, she was disruptive and rude at school; then she had become silly.

Children who spend their school days with their chairs turned strategically away from their teachers may become young people who are quite unable to lend a hand at home. Other teenagers go to more elaborate lengths than is usual to avoid doing any homework. Their books are continually left at home or at school, are lost or even destroyed – and they gravitate to the most unruly part of any classroom at any school. This may be familiar enough behaviour, but it is the degree and consistency of avoidance which seems important. It is true to say that far more energy and work may be thrown into avoiding a task than would actually be required to complete it in the first place. It would appear that negative avoidance behaviour can reinforce itself.

It is interesting that it is the pressure and demands that are being resisted rather than the actual work. The person who avoids demands may well work extremely hard at something, as long as he has chosen to do it, yet he might even have difficulty with someone offering him help or suggesting that he closes a window. He has a need to be in control.

It may be thought that the sort of behaviour which I have been describing is typical of that of young people who are in a rebellious mood or who just feel a little self-conscious and are finding their feet. This may be so, but people with an avoidance problem are not merely feeling awkward or anti this and that; those who are close to them might be able to see that the difficulties are different and more enduring. We may need to reconsider the situation when we automatically call somebody bone idle, totally self-centred or crafty – irritating though this behaviour might be.

ANXIETY, SWITCHING OFF AND AVOIDANCE

Does anxiety cause switching off and avoidance? Anxiety may be a result of such behaviour (see p.135) but it seems sensible to consider that it might also be a cause. Whatever the truth of the matter may be, when questions are asked regarding the personality of a child who exhibits these traits, it generally becomes clear that there are, or have been, symptoms which can be associated with excess tension or anxiety, as I hope will become apparent.

It would seem reasonable to hypothesise that some infants might switch off because the behaviour is pleasurable or genetically programmed. At least in the more extreme cases of withdrawal, however, it is conceivable that tension, anxiety or fear, perhaps with attendant hypersensitivities, might activate, or create an early preference for, a retreat into one's own world – or possibly even create a need to restore the fetal environment or maintain fetal habits. An accompanying severe switch-off or shutdown in the processing of external information (which may become involuntary or the status quo) makes much of the world incomprehensible – and hence creates more anxiety and fear.

Terms of Reference – Anxiety

When referring to anxiety throughout this book, I do not restrict its meaning to imply great fear, worry or stress. I use the word broadly to include mild states of tension – which may result in excess excitement, slightly exaggerated intensity of feeling, restlessness or even a little seriousness. Whilst I include 'tension' in 'anxiety' I shall refer to both words since tension is of value for its specificity, in describing pent-up or unreleased mental energy.

Tension or anxiety is a necessary component of a person and has positive value. But this desirable attribute can be responsible for varying degrees of undesirable behaviour which perhaps has the propensity to occur in many of us.

Conditioning

Behaviour which is instigated by some sort of tension or anxiety might often be sustained, at least in part, by conditioning and programming of the brain. Through conditioning, our brains provide us with immediate responses to familiar situations. Hence it might not be necessary for a child to display obvious signs of tension or anxiety to be suffering from symptoms which result from its effect at an earlier time.

Some years ago my husband and I owned two mules named Gingerfigs and Martha. The larger of the two, Gingerfigs, came to us when she was seven years old. We purchased her from a gentle, kindly couple who had owned her for five years. Prior to this she had belonged to some gypsies. Whilst she had a nice temperament, drew a trap safely and competently and was safe to ride, this mule had a few conditioned reactions. The most problematic of these involved having a head collar put on in order for her to leave a field. Desperate though she would be to leave an enclosure and be taken out for a jaunt, especially once her friend Martha had left ahead of her, Gingerfigs displayed panic reactions, advancing and retreating numerous times before she could eventually manage to brave the ordeal. Even then, she would stand tensely, rigid and twitching. The more open the field and its gateway, the greater was the problem. The difficulty did not exist for the mule if the field led into a very narrow enclosure where she could already feel 'caught'. The reaction had been programmed early in her life and was so strong that a great deal of motivation and determination was required on the part of Gingerfigs to enable her to confront the unpleasant sensations. I am pleased to say that her symptoms have abated and she has become somewhat desensitised with time, and with the patience of her various owners.

It is perhaps easier to recognise conditioned reactions in animals than in humans, who are more complex in their behaviour. Nevertheless, children (as well as adults) experience degrees of conditioning. The behaviour is easily misinterpreted.

ENVIRONMENTAL AND PRENATAL INFLUENCES

No one can doubt that environmental influences contribute to anxiety levels and one's emotional state and there is no intention of refuting their importance in not making them a subject of this book. There is much compelling literature on the significance to child development of positive early interaction between children and their carers. Moreover, child abuse and other traumatic events can result in symptoms of anxiety, as may lesser happenings. When considering anxiety we must of course remain vigilant and be aware of and sensitive to anxiety provoking influences and it is assumed in the chapters which follow, that they would undergo proper consideration and that families would receive help, when necessary, from appropriate professions.

An additional factor is the effect of prenatal stress. There is increasing evidence that a pregnant woman's stress hormones can affect the fetus and have long-lasting effects on the child's behaviour. Prenatally stressed infants show a higher incidence of attention deficits, hyperanxiety and disturbed social behaviour; it also appears that they may be more prone to future psychiatric disorders (Weinstock, 1997). Wadhwa and colleagues have found that, independent of biomedical risk, maternal prenatal stress factors are significantly associated with low infant birth weight and preterm birth (Wadhwa et al., 1993). Van Reempts and his colleagues suggest that, following chronic intrauterine stress, there is a change in the maturation of the autonomic nervous system which could make infants more vulnerable in stressful situations (Van Reempts et al., 1996).

***

Switching off is common among young children. It is more than simply not listening properly or not paying attention in the manner, for example, of a hyperactive child. It may become the habitual or involuntary shutting out of information. It might be slight and occasional with few, if any, troublesome effects. At the other extreme, the child may seem quite detached from the business of the world. His thinking may be slow or delayed and perhaps channelled in one direction only, so that he is unable to connect ideas and appreciate meanings and consequences. As we shall see later, he may not even think at all. The behaviour might be apparent soon after birth or it may seem to develop in early childhood.

Switching off and avoiding are not, however, entirely negative aspects of behaviour and surely most of us participate in these activities to some degree. I began this chapter by referring to the relaxing effects of daydreaming. Switching off and avoiding would seem to have a protective function, at least initially. Professionals working with children can learn a lot by talking to adults who have the ability to switch off quite deeply and are willing to describe the warm, pleasurable sensations which can be experienced.

It does appear that focusing one's attention completely and shutting out all distracting thoughts and goings-on around one can be conducive to outstanding achievement. Withdrawal behaviour, however, may be capable of going further in this respect for it is sometimes associated with the development of extraordinary powers (Chapters Three and Nine).

Switching off and avoidance behaviour are personality traits of such importance that I have allocated this chapter to them alone. Many traits arise from them. I shall look at these, and others, in the next two chapters. Once we have established the significance and prevalence of all the various traits, we shall be able to see how tension or anxiety can actually be a causal factor in many speech, language, learning and social difficulties.

Whether anxiety is severe, moderate or slight, behavioural traits may attend it. Since a certain amount of anxiety is normal and healthy, I shall often be seen to be depicting normal behaviour. When the behaviour is abnormal, it is usually only a matter of degree.

CHAPTER THREE

OTHER PERSONALITY TRAITS

The difficulty with getting people to look carefully at personality traits in young children is that most of these traits are so common that they are dismissed as forming a part of normal childhood behaviour, which indeed they do. The degree to which children manifest traits is of course highly variable. When one concerned and exhausted mother tells another parent that her boy, Mark, gets into dreadful tempers and is very stubborn she is likely to be told something like "Oh, so does my Patrick and he's awfully stubborn too." But a fly on the wall at Mark's home would see a quite different scene from a fly on the wall at Patrick's, whose tempers are a relatively mild affair. Similarly, one child may be rather faddy concerning his food; another a 'nightmare' to feed.

Many parents suffer in silence. They have their pride, do not wish to appear inadequate, and usually try to avoid criticising their children while speaking with other people. Let us suppose that a mother grumbles about her child growing bored *very* easily. Might not a listening acquaintance or friend be likely to suspect that it is the mother's fault? When he is at this confidant's house (where there are plenty of novel and exciting things) he seems quite the perfect boy – perhaps spirited but what can be wrong with that?

The traits of switching off and avoiding have already been discussed. Let us now look at some other traits which I have repeatedly encountered in my speech and language therapy clinics. Many children exhibit a number of the traits mentioned in this chapter; probably all children show one or two to at least a mild degree. As will be noticed throughout this book, the traits tend to be interrelated. To understand a trait in relation to a particular child, it is generally necessary to consider all of his other ones, too, in order to form a whole, composite picture.

Sometimes I shall give alternative possible explanations for a particular kind of behaviour but I do not claim that the explanations offered below are exhaustive. Moreover, little reference will be made to the role played by brain damage or hearing losses and to disorders with a purely physical origin. Such influences, and their emotional effects, will be taken for granted in this book.

Inactivity

Some parents find that their babies are "very good". Perhaps an infant spends most of his time just sitting inertly and staring. But then it may be a long time before he walks and he might not seem to be very curious. Maybe he never crawled and very likely he is not talking, either. The parents of these children often encounter difficulties a little later on. Such a baby might well be switched off to his environment to some degree. As he grows older, conflicts may arise within him. He becomes more interested in the world and more involved in it but may remain reticent and he has developed reactions which are often difficult for him to change. When I have asked a mother if her child was a good baby the reply has often been, "Oh yes, *very* good but later he changed!" The very good, reticent baby need not be switched off, however. He may be observant and take a great deal of healthy interest in his surroundings in a passive way.

I do not necessarily include in this category children who have a learning disability as a result of brain damage or malfunction, or some genetic aberration, although they too, are likely to be less active. Whilst the inactivity of some of these children may be due to them distancing themselves from their environment, there are likely to be other causes.

Aloofness

Preoccupied children and those who are switched off or less involved in their surroundings tend to exhibit varying degrees of aloofness. It might be that they merely seem rather indifferent to cuddles. At the other extreme they may fail to relate to people as persons, although they may lead them around to do things for them – using them rather as a tool. Some may not cry, smile or laugh, having greatly restricted emotions and emotional involvement with others.

Clumsiness

Clumsiness is frequently associated with inattention and perhaps with a state of tension or not being properly tuned in regarding one's kinaesthetic sensation and spatial awareness. Sometimes clumsiness can be, at least in part, the result of impulsive behaviour, particularly in a child who displays the Attention Deficit Hyperactivity Disorder (Chapter Seven). It might even be attributable to or exacerbated by a tendency to try too hard at an activity, so that one is making a great effort in an overly tense state.

The young child may exhibit poor timing in his movements, have difficulty catching a ball, drawing, throwing and hopping and seem heavy on his feet. Perhaps he keeps dropping things and uses too much physical force sometimes but is rather 'floppy' at other times. Personality-related factors might be at least partly responsible – possibly causing the early programming of unrefined or dyspraxic motor responses which can persist as a person's norm (rather as problems can persist when a squint is treated late because the child's brain has become fixed in its behaviour).

I should also like to mention dribbling here, for a young child who seems to be always falling over and bumping into things through lack of attention or awareness may be prone to dribbling, too. He may simply be unaware of, or unconcerned about his saliva and the position of his tongue and lips. As awareness develops, dribbling ceases.

Fearfulness

Everyone needs to have caution; we would not live long without it. Alas, some children are terrified by loud noises or the slightest unusual sight or sound and sometimes fears may be quite irrational. Reaction to traffic can be informative. A child who is considerably frightened by the sight and sound of cars and lorries rushing past may keep his distance, scraping his body against the side of a wall as he walks along, tightly gripping his mother's hand. Another child might walk straight out in front of a car without looking because he is switched off in a general way, to a degree. (One seven-year-old who attended for therapy did exactly this and was knocked down.)

Sometimes a child will be quite frightened by a visit to a speech and language therapy department, especially if it is the first time he has come. He may react by looking anxiously around the building or room, appearing to take in everything he sees and hears. Even after several visits he may panic if he hears a workman banging somewhere in the building.

Often the frightened child suffers from nightmares and will not sleep in his own bed. Perhaps he insists on getting in with his mother and father in the middle of the night or will not go to bed until everyone else does. This may seem like the case of a spoilt child with bad habits and 'soft' parents but when a child is desperate, his parents may have little choice in the matter. The poet Samuel Taylor Coleridge, who suffered with manic-depressive symptoms, was well able to understand his daughter Sara's childhood night-time fears. In her memoirs Sara wrote, "He insisted that a lighted candle should be left in my room, in the interval between my retiring to bed and Mama's joining me. From that time forth my sufferings ceased." (Coleridge, 1875). Sara, however, like her father, was mentally ill for much of her adult life.

One child may be frightened of running water while another screams in fear whenever he is travelling in a car. When a fear is very strong we may talk about phobias – and even very young children can be petrified by spiders. Yet it is so often the little happenings which can alert parents to a slight excess of anxiety in their child. Perhaps he buries himself in his mother's bosom throughout a pantomime, for instance, or worries about going to, or being late for school or even about his health. Although such behaviour is common, it should be noted.

Worrying

Sometimes a child worries about things a great deal. We find adults, too, who worry persistently and perhaps even compulsively about trivia (yet may take relative catastrophes in their stride). In their book, *Attention Deficit Disorder*, Edward Hallowell and John Ratey maintain that some people actually use worry as a means of organising their thinking and preventing a chaotic mind.

Rituals, Routines, Order and Sameness

Children who are fond of rituals, routine, order or sameness are commonly seen in a speech and language clinic – and the variations on the theme are endless. There may be a slight resistance to change on the one hand, and demands for sameness so extreme on the other that an entire family's day is organised around the child, for the sake of peace and quiet. These children may be giving themselves more security by restricting the amount of change in their world, but often it appears that tension or anxiety is resulting in obsessive-compulsive behaviour. Interestingly, it is not uncommon for celebrities to engage in ritualistic behaviour before going on stage, and top tennis players are sometimes seen seeking solace in rituals during tense moments on court. Likewise, people in dangerous situations frequently behave ritualistically or superstitiously. But let us look at some examples of rituals, routine, order and sameness in children.

Gavin insists that he and his mother walk exactly the same way to play-group – even to the point that she goes down the steps on the left side while he keeps to the right, the railings dividing them. On the way back they must still walk up their own side of the steps. When her father leaves the house in the mornings to go to work, Clara kisses him in a very particular manner and then insists that he returns the kisses in the same mode – first on the fore-head, then her left cheek and finally her right one. He and Clara's big brother must wave to her as she stands at the window, too, or she will be very distressed. Gerard will not allow his mother to help out at playgroup. She does not normally stay so she must not ever stay – it breaks the rule. He carries the same little bag around with him all day every day and he seems to have a compulsion to hit other children for no apparent reason. Abigail arrives at the clinic in a party frock. "Oh, who's a lucky girl? Are you going somewhere nice, Abigail?" No, she has been wearing the dress for a fortnight. Toby has to have his breakfast (which is always the same) at exactly the same time each day – or he will refuse to eat anything at all. And lunch must be a hot one. If Kenton and his mother go shopping they have to be back by 3.30pm. – that is tea-time. (Naturally his mother finds this somewhat restricting.) Emma insists on the same brand of biscuits and Shashida always turns all the baked bean tins around to face exactly the same way in the supermarket. Every bed-time (which is always at the same time), Heather leads her mother upstairs, empties some cupboards and spreads their contents all around the room. Then she looks out of the window and says exactly what she said the night before, and the night before that... Alan watches the same video again and again; if his father tries to fast-forward it he knows exactly what has been omitted, and objects. Graham spins whatever he can get to spin and Guy always walks on his toes. Darius flaps his hands very repetitively. (He is also prone to standing astride a door and moving it to and fro between the palms of his hands while he carefully watches and absorbs himself in its movement.) Adrian lines up his cars but does not otherwise play with them and Jonathan will not see an ornament out of place. Jacob insists on having the same plate and cup and will only eat chops in Sheffield. Rose must be told the same story every day, in exactly the same way, and she collects little bits of paper from wherever she can find them. Jimmy travels on his bike around the park in the same direction each day while his mother stands next to a bench (but must never sit on it) – and she must smoke a cigarette while she stands there. Cheryl keeps repeating what somebody has just said to her.

I could go on and on... Typically the child has more than one ritual and I am sure plenty of parents could add to this list.

It seems appropriate to consider tics (or habit spasms) in this section. They include repetitive eye blinking, eye rolling, nose twitching, sniffing, throat clearing, repeating something like "mm", head jerking, hand or thumb twisting, shoulder shrugging, etc. These acts become compulsive and automatic although they might, with effort, be controlled for a limited period of time. Sometimes there may be a compulsion to jump, smell or keep touching things, to yell out or do something forbidden or to bite or hit oneself. Tics can come and go and increase with stress. There are features in stammering which remind one of tics, and occasionally an adult who stammers will talk of a feeling of compulsion – that although he wants to be rid of the stammer, he *likes* to do it, and feels he *has* to (p.57).

Tourette syndrome is a term used to describe serious cases of tics. Since tics are often associated with a fear of doing something ridiculous or rude in public, a child suffering from the syndrome is likely to be old enough to have an awareness of social taboos. Features which frequently accompany tics include rituals, hyperactivity, learning and behavioural difficulties and sleep disorders. There is indeed a lot of overlapping of symptoms between the syndrome and other conditions. Furthermore, one member of a family might exhibit tics, another rituals and obsessions, etc. It is clear that Tourette syndrome does not exist as an entity which is independent of other conditions.

Obsessions

Speech and language therapists sometimes encounter a child who delights in talking about one particular subject only – be it cars, bikes, trains, lawn mowers, balls, registration numbers or a specific television programme or video. He may draw nothing but pictures of trains and appear to think of little else. Sometimes one obsession is suddenly abandoned for another. It may be only natural for children to love these things but I am referring to the child who is continually harking back to his subject. Obsessional behaviour is known to be associated with compulsion and anxiety.

Fussiness

Sometimes a child is anxious not to get his hands or clothes dirty or will display unusual fussiness for his age in some other area. (I have already referred to the youngster who cannot tolerate objects being moved out of place.) Fussy streaks may take the form of very methodical, orderly behaviour or perfectionism. They may sometimes be associated with a strong adherence to rules (Chapter Four).

A child who is exacting may require specific behaviour from others. If a friend displeases him in some way he might send him away or withdraw from him.

Comforters

Some children rock themselves or grind their teeth to comfort or calm themselves and release tension (in some cases perhaps replacing outside noise or confusion with predictable, orderly movement). Such behaviour is generally interpreted as a sign of tension or anxiety although one might sometimes view it as stemming from a lack of mental occupation and a paucity of thought. Other children may bang their heads rhythmically against their cots or beds while they go off to sleep. Plenty suck a thumb, dummy, a particular piece of rag or a blanket. Some are desperately fond of a cuddly toy from which they refuse to be parted. They may object to their favoured item being washed, preferring to have its familiar scent retained. Perhaps, however, there is a little extra anxiety in the child who *always* seems to be sucking his thumb, for example, or who still cannot be separated easily from his toy or blanket when he is rather older.

Sometimes excitement, such as that generated by Christmas, can increase tension and thumb-sucking or other repetitive behaviour or speech.

A child who walks around holding something is not necessarily using the item as a comforter. It might be related to an obsession or the activity may be ritualistic. Some children may ensure that their hands are occupied to help them resist demands or physical contact.

Chewing

Many youngsters, such as the restless, fidgety, hyperactive ones, seem to be continually putting things into their mouths and chewing them; they are not always teething. This may be another outlet for excess tension.

Sleeping Habits

Sleeping habits are sometimes a clue to anxiety levels. The child who sleeps fitfully, or does not seem to need as much sleep as the rest of the family, may be a tense or anxious person. He might be prone to nightmares and possibly to sleepwalking too. Perhaps he will not settle down to sleep until his parents come up to bed, or as soon as he awakens he calls out for his mother, needing to know where she is. Maybe he refuses to sleep alone. Such behaviour may result directly from fears, where it is not habitual or ritualistic. A child may even be afraid to go to sleep, feeling that he must stay awake to be on guard against some evil. It might be advisable to look for other signs of anxiety in his present or past behaviour.

Eating Habits

Tense or anxious children sometimes binge – maybe devouring huge quantities of one particular food, be it satsumas, biscuits or yoghurt, and nothing besides. On the other hand, they may eat or drink next to nothing and greatly worry their parents. *Why?* If they show a strong preference for a specific food or drink it might be a matter of sameness. Or possibly they have developed a dependency on it. If they barely eat at all there may be a resistance to accept something new, but perhaps they are reacting to people's demands – the demanding of them that they should eat. One might compare this aspect of their behaviour with other aspects to see if the situation becomes clearer. A child might even become resistant to coming to the dinner table. This may seem like wilfulness yet might be behaviour which he feels compelled to exhibit. In some cases there is a fear of eating in front of (or being watched by) others.

Sometimes a child will only eat foods of a certain texture. Perhaps he will not eat anything hard, for example. One little girl refused all hard foods until she went to a respite centre for a week. Here she happily ate hard biscuits – it did not break her rule to eat hard food away from home.

Some underweight, withdrawing children appear to have a suppressed appetite. They never show hunger or thirst. (These youngsters may not react to pain or temperature, or their reactions to the stimuli might be delayed. They may not exhibit proper emotions either.) It seems that such children have prevented themselves from experiencing the sensations or from being able to interpret them correctly (see page 103).

Other rather tense or anxious children may simply eat large quantities of anything edible. This behaviour might seem to have a compulsive element although food is perhaps a comfort for them. The hyperactive youngster may have a voracious appetite and gobble food in the same spirit with which he rushes into most other things.

A child may retain infantile patterns of swallowing with the tongue thrust forward. Lack of awareness (or involvement) and a liking for sameness are possible causes of retention. Poor inhibition of infantile reflexes can be associated with a withdrawing personality. Donna Williams, a sufferer from autism and campaigner for a better understanding of it, relates how she was surprised to learn that most of the infantile reflexes were still uninhibited in her when she was approaching the age of thirty (*Autism: An Inside-Out Approach, 1996*).

Walking Habits

Some children's rituals extend to walking on their toes – and they are reluctant to change the habit. Continually telling the child to walk properly does not seem to be effective. In fact he expects the correction and it may become part of his routine. It might be better to remove any causes of stress, as far as is possible (although high anxiety levels may exist without any provocation), and simply suggest from time to time, that he walks like other people do, for the sake of his legs as well as appearances. He may begin to walk normally of his own accord, however. Toe-walking is not uncommon among children who withdraw.

Some other children may walk with a stiff leg or slide around – and their movements can mimic some physical deformity. Sometimes hips are errone-ously suspected of being faulty. The variation in manner of walking is great and there may be accompanying rhythmic arm movements. Then the unfortunate child is often supposed brain-damaged.

Feelings of disconnection, such as can occur in autism, may give rise to unco-ordinated movement.

Wetting and Soiling

It is generally accepted that wetting and soiling can be related to the emotions. We know that some anxious children regress in their toilet training. Maybe growing up is bringing them too much involvement, too many demands. Bed-wetting (nocturnal enuresis) is an involuntary habit of passing urine at night and is common among children who are feeling anxious.

Sometimes a child who withdraws is prevented from having an awareness of the need to visit the toilet. Furthermore, deliberate wetting or soiling can be part of a learning process whereby a globally switched off, withdrawn child becomes more aware of his body and identifies with it. Sometimes there is a fear of passing urine or motions or of visiting the toilet itself.

Like the rest of the body, the urinary tracts, stomach and intestines can be affected by responses to emotion. Indeed, a somatic manifestation of emotional tension may be associated with any part of the body via overactivity of the autonomic nervous system. It may take the form of stomach upsets, vomiting, an urge to pass urine more frequently, and various degrees of diarrhoea or constipation. It may be, as we are sometimes told, normal for there to be great variation between one person's frequency of bowel movements and another's, but we might say too, that there is great variation between states of tension and responses to them.

Hyperactivity

This characteristic in a child keeps parents very busy. The youngster has a hyperactive mind and shows it in his actions. He is excited first by one thing, then by another. He is like a wound up spring. He fidgets and he fiddles with ornaments, his clothing – with anything in sight. He is either inattentive to what you say or takes it all in at lightning speed and is off on his next activity. He may exhibit poor kinaesthetic or spatial awareness, be impulsive and pay little attention to the timing or execution of his physical activities, so that clumsiness might ensue. He is easily distracted and he does not tend to play imaginatively. He may show extremes of enthusiasm and boredom, and *hypo*activity at times, when he might just lie sucking his thumb – perhaps if the world has failed to produce anything exciting during the past few minutes or so. Maybe he has what seems like an insatiable appetite for food or new experiences. He might sometimes be a step ahead of his parents and difficult to surprise, having quickly anticipated exciting events. He tends to be egocentric and hence somewhat socially unaware. He overreacts, has a 'short fuse' and a very low level of tolerance. He is far from patient, wishing everything done yesterday, and has difficulty sustaining his interest, his brain often appearing to race on to the next thing. His concentration can be intense, for a rather limited period, or extremely poor, depending on how interested he is in the subject and how exciting it is for him.

I have just attempted to sketch some common manifestations of hyperactivity. No hyperactive child behaves in quite the same way as another and in many respects one youngster might even seem totally different from another but one has the impression that there is a lot of tension-related energy within these children.

It does not follow that, because he is hyperactive during the day, the child will necessarily have sleep problems. He may do, but he may sleep very well, which is a consolation for his parents. Another consolation for many parents of hyperactive children is that their uninhibited enthusiasm and positive enjoyment of some things, however short-lived, can be a delight to witness – although they are capable of showing an equal degree of misery.

Hyperactivity is discussed in further detail in Chapter Seven.

Speech and Language Traits

Speech and language development, including the child's ability to understand, is affected by withdrawal, anxiety and tension in so many different ways that it merits a chapter of its own (Chapter Four).

Sense of Danger

Some children have a very poor sense of danger for their age. They may be switched off to it, or simply preoccupied. Moreover, if they were to fall, they might not put out their arms properly to save themselves. I have seen an inattentive, hyperactive child running over high, jagged rocks which were covered with slippery seaweed – with his hands in his pockets. (Parents of a child like this should not be persuaded by other people to turn a blind eye to such sights. Their concern is perfectly reasonable and they are not being overprotective. They know their child best and it is entirely sensible to wish to avoid a trip to a casualty department.)

There is also the child who, oblivious to danger, may carry out physical feats in a single-minded, uninhibited and agile way.

Another risk with the switched off, uninvolved child is of him wandering from home and going off with strangers. Poor social awareness, sometimes coupled with an inability to discriminate between a parent's advice or instruction and anyone else's, makes him more vulnerable, so that vigilance is required for longer than would usually be necessary.

Dressing Difficulties

The hyperactive, inattentive child may well put his T-shirt on back to front and inside out. He may even do it knowingly, in the cause of speed, if his priorities lie elsewhere. A rather globally switched off youngster may have more serious dressing difficulties. He may not seem to have a clue where to begin and he may be painfully slow – which contrasts sharply with the often tornado-like action of the impatient, hyperactive child. Sometimes a highly dependent child will seem incapable of dressing himself yet be able to put on clothes from a dressing-up box.

Hearing

A child who is switched off to some degree may appear to have a hearing difficulty – but his parents are usually aware that he seems to be able to hear very well on occasions.

An anxious or switched off child sometimes exhibits extremely acute hearing or hyperacusis (see Hypersensitivity).

'Selfishness'

Sometimes a mother will complain that her son or daughter seems selfish or maybe even callous. He appears to be totally unaffected by anyone else's suffering and might actually be quite spiteful. Of course, all little children are self-centred, but these parents are referring to what seems to them to be a real lack of feeling or empathy. One mother was worried because her four-year-old kept emptying bottles of shampoo into the bath; no matter how upset she showed herself to be, such habits continued. Acts like these may be rituals and a parent's reactions may be part of the ritual but sometimes the youngster appears to have cut himself off from the emotions and demands (or appeals) of those around him. And his shutting-out behaviour may well prevent him from understanding the significance of what he is doing.

A child may be switched off and perhaps fail to use eye contact to the extent that he is unable to read facial expressions, which of course aid us in appreciating the feelings of others. They may be quite meaningless and confusing to him, for an understanding of them requires an association or connection of ideas. Furthermore, it is only to be expected that he will have difficulty comprehending those feelings in others which he is prevented from experiencing with understanding in himself. (He may eventually set about learning facial expressions in a rather rigid, mechanical way; he might approach someone who is grimacing and ask, "Are you happy?")

Egocentricity

It may be that a child does not really seem selfish so much as egocentric. For example, the hyperactive youngster, or an apprehensive or serious child, may be so occupied by his own activities or thoughts that he does not consider what others are doing or thinking. Egocentricity naturally creates social difficulties but it is often outgrown, at least in part, as the child matures. If obvious social difficulties persist, the person is likely to be switched off in some measure.

Convulsions

Convulsions are common in childhood and are triggered by irritation or disturbance in the brain, as can occur with a brain injury or a sudden rise in temperature during a fever. Or this additional stimulation of the brain can be caused by *emotional* factors. Convulsions can indeed occur after a sudden fright or some anxiety and, it might be sensible to surmise, perhaps recur with less provocation once the brain has learned to react in this manner. I do not mean to imply that a child who has had a convulsion following a great shock is at risk of developing regular seizures. If his fright was reasonable, there is no cause for alarm, although his convulsion does suggest that his anxiety levels might be quite high.

Breath-holding attacks during emotional outbursts are not uncommon in young children. The distraught child suddenly stops breathing and may hold his breath so long that he turns blue in the face. These attacks are not life-threatening and the little child starts breathing again of his own accord, even if he has turned quite blue first. Fortunately, the problem tends to disappear before school age but it is wise to avoid a dramatic reaction to any such episode for sometimes this withholding of breath brings on a convulsion. Excessive emotional stimulation has actually caused a convulsive fit to occur.

Some forms of epilepsy are characterised by convulsions but there are forms in which there are no convulsive spasms at all. There may be a momentary disturbance of consciousness which can show itself in a blank look which lasts but a few seconds. As with convulsive epilepsy, such absences are not uncommon among children who withdraw; this can make them hard to distinguish from some switching off behaviour.

Lancman and his colleagues (1994) report significant familial or personal distress in 81.4 per cent of children and adolescents with psychogenic seizures.

We all have the potential to experience a seizure but our susceptibility to them varies according to our threshold level. It may well be that a low seizure threshold is sometimes related to high anxiety levels. Grant (1985) comments on certain epileptic patients' vulnerability to convulsions in response to acute emotional upheaval or certain types of cognitive challenges. He remarks on the probability that social stress and emotional tension can produce lowering of seizure threshold by increasing levels of fatigue and disrupting sleep.

Handedness

Tense, agitated or switched off children appear to be more prone to an undetermined hand preference and to left-handedness. Maybe they use their right hand for one activity, their left for another, or alternate in the use of their hands for a particular activity, such as drawing or writing. They may also hold a pencil more awkwardly than is usual.

Before we blame handedness, undetermined hand and eye preferences or eye/hand co-ordination directly for literacy difficulties, etc., perhaps we should not entirely rule out the possibility that the child's personality has had some influence on these factors as well as on his literacy skills. (Literacy problems will be discussed in Chapter Six.)

K.M. Cornish and I.C. McManus (1996) have compared handedness in children with autism, children with learning disabilities, and control school-children. They found the normal controls to be more lateralised and more consistent in their hand preference than either of the other groups (and as might be expected, the younger children were less consistent than the older ones). A left-handed preference was shown by 23 per cent of children with autism, 11.5 per cent of children with learning disability and 4.4 per cent of normal control children. This incidence of left-handedness in the groups was found to be consistent with that reported elsewhere (Fein et al., 1984).

Vision

Some children seem visually inattentive or switched off. They may misinterpret simple pictures, fail to notice visual detail, persist in attempting jigsaws in an entirely trial and error manner, or complete them according to their shapes without utilising clues from their pictures. (Some children prefer to complete jigsaws picture face downward.) There is sometimes a great interest in visual detail and patterns while their meaning or significance is not attended to. Seeing things and people in bits as a result of focusing on small details, or viewing them according to certain fixed criteria, may cause problems in recognition – such as when a person stands who normally sits. There may be difficulties when someone moves an item of furniture or fails to wear his usual clothing.

It may sometimes be the case that an anxious or switched off child's visual perception is heightened or distorted (see Hypersensitivity). This would account for some children staring intently at pictures, etc., or avoiding them altogether.

Sometimes a dyslexic child will say that his eyes become blurred when he tries to read or learn a spelling; as will be seen in Chapter Six, such a problem is likely to be anxiety-related.

Anxious children may well adopt idiosyncratic characteristics related to their vision, and eye contact is lacking in or avoided by some. Switched off children may have a distant-looking or 'empty' stare, which can serve as a shutting out mechanism. In a study combining a medical team with psychologists, Douche et al. (1990) concluded that strabismus (squints) can have an emotional origin. Squints are indeed common among anxious children.

Temper Tantrums

Most young children can get into a paddy when they fail to get their own way but some throw extreme tantrums. We have already considered breath-holding during emotional outbursts and how children sometimes turn blue (see Convulsions). It may also happen that the child becomes quite aggressive – biting and hitting other people (or himself) and maybe throwing things. He may overbreathe (hyperventilate), make his body rigid, or emit a high pitched squeal. He might even vomit.

There are, of course, always reasons for outbursts, even if they are simply habitual or release pent-up energy or tension, but if the child has a less than straightforward personality, his parents' reasoning may naturally fall short at times.

We have also considered the inattentive, hyperactive child who overreacts to anything which fails to suit him. Both his pleasure and his fury seem to have a very wide boundary and egocentricity does nothing to curb his reactions. He may even awaken from his daily nap in a temper – at times his level of tolerance seems to be zero. There appears to be a high level of tension within him and if we look for deep psychological reasons for his outbursts we may well fail to find any.

If tempestuous behaviour is related to compulsive activity, it is all the more important to be aware of what is going on when the child becomes distraught. The youngster will perhaps be more likely to give up harmful rituals if steps can be taken which reduce his anxiety – and maturation may help him, too. It is conceivable that simply interfering with them could make him practise them more or develop more problematic ones. On the other hand, a potentially serious ritual or habit might be removed if it could be sensitively discouraged in its very early stages. Each case is highly individual, so that any cast-iron advice would be irresponsible. If we are sensitively aware of a child's behaviour we shall have an improved understanding of it and how to deal with it.

It is sometimes difficult for us to distinguish between fear, anger and pain when an infant is screaming, especially in novel situations. It may be, for example, that in many cases where we assume an infant is suffering from colic, he is actually crying in fear. Furthermore, if he does have colic, it might be induced by fear (see Wetting and Soiling). Heightened sensory experiences are sometimes the cause of emotional outbursts (see Hypersensitivity).

Poor understanding, which will be discussed in the following chapter, may be at the root of many a temper, and we need to bear in mind that some young children (and even some much older ones), seem unaware that other people do not share their knowledge (p.51). Unintelligibility can cause frustration for the child, too.

A child may become angry and even aggressive when people do not abide by his rigid 'rules'. He appears stubborn and may be labelled spoilt but his behaviour is driven by a need for others to conform.

Dependency

Sometimes a child seems unable to play or do anything else without his mother's, or even a relative stranger's help or presence. This may well be ritualised behaviour (perhaps originally associated with a reluctance to grow up or accept change). Possibly he is frightened of being left alone or of not knowing where someone is.

A school child with learning difficulties may seem incapable of working without his personal classroom assistant, or a youngster might become very possessive of a parent, and object whenever his mother or father pays any attention to a sibling. Often a child is found to interrupt whenever his mother is speaking on the telephone.

Independence

I have met several children who rather compulsively insist on doing things themselves. For example, every time he is helped into a car, a child may get out again and then get in under his own steam. This behaviour may be related to keeping the status quo, or sameness again, or it might be viewed as being associated with an avoidance of demands or involvement.

Sometimes the child is unable to continue with an activity when a parent enters the room; he may even have a conditioned panic attack. A reaction to sensory stimulation might be a factor here (see Hypersensitivity) but a child may display independent behaviour as a result of anxiety about social situations and others watching what he is doing. To describe him as shy or embarrassed might be an unfortunate understatement. Such feelings may of course result in avoidance of demands.

Retardation

It will be appreciated that a child might refuse to dress himself or seem unable to because he is reluctant to change or grow up. Often such a child's speech and language development is delayed, as may be his toilet training or some other behaviour.

Regression

It is quite common for children to regress in their speech, toilet training and general behaviour when they are feeling anxious. Sometimes the regression is related to family changes or to extra demands being made on a child.

Parents tell of children who have become upset when looking at photographs of themselves as babies, saying that they wish they could be a baby again.

Sensitivity to Criticism

A large number of children are very sensitive to criticism. They may become weepy or appear to sulk or be hurt at the slightest reprimand or suggestion that they have not acted as well as they might have done. They would perhaps rather opt out altogether, and maybe switch off, than risk failure. Older school children, in particular, may give few clues to their true feelings, so that their sensitivity might not be appreciated. Sensitive children can be particularly susceptible to adverse comments from their peers.

Allergies

Many young children are prone to allergies and susceptibility to them has a strong genetic component. Any allergy can be exacerbated by emotional disturbance and indeed, emotion may in some cases be the principal factor in their occurrence.

Asthma affects approximately ten per cent of children and it is more prevalent among boys than girls; allergens and emotion are frequent triggers. Agarwal and Sethi (1978), using objective methods of evaluation to determine the presence of underlying emotional factors in bronchial asthma, found asthmatics and allergic people to be more serious, tense, emotionally unstable and neurotic than normal controls.

Stress or emotion may cause our bodies to be in a state of overreaction – so we might initially acquire our allergies during periods when our immune system is overly sensitive. Many researchers are investigating the relationship between stress, depression and the immune system. The brain's likely involvement in immune system regulation and suppressed and excessive immune reactions are discussed in two papers by P.H. Black (1994) of Boston University School of Medicine. He reports findings that, after an initial transient boost to immune system functioning, stress induces immunosuppression, enhances disease acquisition and reactivates latent disease. He also reports that stress can activate an inflammatory response and may be a factor in the cause and/or progression of some inflammatory diseases. Moreover, he refers to a study in which introverts were more susceptible than extroverts to viral infections (Totman et al., 1980). A study by Kunzendorf and Butler (1986) suggests that mania and schizophrenia may promote immune hyperactivity or allergy and defend the body against depression and immune deficiency.

The underlying mechanisms are highly complex but it may be that a genetic component of allergies is related to anxiety.

Hypersensitivity

Some children can be hypersensitive to *emotion* and are at pains to avoid it. They might avoid social contact, show extreme embarrassment or avoid the self-exposure that making choices or creating pictures necessitates.

Anxious people may be hypersensitive (allergic) to certain foods or chemicals. Or they may experience *sensory* hypersensitivity. This may take the form of excessive sensitivity of the skin, abnormally acute hearing (hyperacusis), heightened or distorted visual perception or indeed, any other heightening of sensation. In a book on the subject of manic-depressive illness, *Touched with Fire*, psychiatrist and manic-depressive sufferer Kay Redfield Jamison (1996) refers to the intensified perceptual awareness, including hyperacusis and increased sensitivity to light, which frequently forms part of mild mania (hypomania) and mania. Whilst sensory hypersensitivities may be enjoyed to a degree and, in the experience of Donna Williams, be addictive, so too may they cause distress and pain.

Williams (1996) believes that sensory hypersensitivity results from her brain reacting to her lack of response to sensory stimuli. She also believes that it can result from taking in more information than can be processed and explains that hearing may become painfully acute if too much effort is made. Obviously a vicious circle might be in operation.

One child may be seen sniffing each page of a book. (This of course may be quite unrelated to hypersensitivity; he may simply be enjoying experiencing the book in this manner.) Another child may cover up his ears to some ordinary sound. He may be troubled by an empty crisp packet which moves in the wind outside a closed window, attentive to the quietest of lawnmowers in the distance or react to any sound coming from the building's plumbing. Sometimes a youngster seems visually inattentive or he stares intensely at everything on a page of a book – possibly his visual perception is heightened or distorted. The significance of such behaviour might be discovered by considering all the individual's personality traits together.

As with other 'hyper' states, the opposite 'hypo' condition may be experienced, too. Whilst at times a child will react to an overwhelming sensation, at others, he might try to intensify a dull one.

Self-directed Abuse

The youngster who acts aggressively towards himself might, for example, bang his head hard against a wall or floor or pull out handfuls of his hair until he has large bald patches. It may be that he bites his hand when he is told off.

When a child blocks out or fails to involve himself with the world he may appear insensitive (or to have delayed responses) to pain and temperature or have difficulty understanding his sensations. This could encourage self-directed abuse, perhaps in the form of experimentation. There may be poor self-awareness, so that feelings of self-preservation might be lacking. In her book, *Nobody Nowhere* (1998), Donna Williams describes how she attacked herself in an effort to escape from her imprisoning body.

As we have seen, a child might keep striking or biting himself as the result of a tic he has developed. Moreover, stress or switching off behaviour may lead to hypersensitivity of the skin which could cause irritation and hence encourage some self-directed aggression in this way (see Hypersensitivity).

The child may of course simply be feeling very angry or tense and need to release his tension or distract himself. Yet another possible explanation for self-directed aggression is self-condemnation and a need to purge oneself. Whatever the reason for it, such behaviour may become compulsive and ritualised. It is even possible that a child might have become addicted to pain.

When considering biochemical imbalance as a possible basic cause of self-directed abuse, it is necessary to bear in mind that emotion or stress may be responsible for such an imbalance.

Traits related to depression

Many of the traits mentioned in this chapter are to be found in depression so that it is important to give depression consideration. The subject is discussed in Chapter Nine where some symptoms of depression in childhood are listed.

Extraordinary Ability

Heightened sensitivity, stress symptoms and withdrawing or withholding the mind in some measure from the external world appears to be sometimes associated with extraordinary ability or savant skills. Some people are indeed able to draw, compose, invent, memorise, absorb information, calculate, mimic, etc., with apparent ease and brilliance, though not necessarily with meaning or significance.

Professor Allan Snyder at the Centre for the Mind in Canberra, Australia, believes that something is turned off rather than on in cases of savant skills in autism. Interestingly, he hypothesises that we all have within us the mental machinery for performing extraordinary feats, but our cortical development interferes with this. In savant children, the mind is less concept driven and has access to lower levels of raw information (Snyder and Mitchell, 1999).

In the case of young children we may discover that padlocks are undone without a key or a clock is dismantled and put together again. Very occasionally a parent will remark on, and be puzzled by, a withdrawn child's abnormal strength – a little three-year-old might be able to pick up an extremely heavy item of furniture, for example. It often seems that certain brain functions are being tapped at the expense or to the neglect of others; occasionally it might appear that 'psi' powers are in operation (Chapter Nine).

A child may show an unusual degree of awareness regarding something that interests him and pay great attention to small details. He might map out particulars in his environment or remember, what may seem to us, insignificant happenings in the past. General unease, fear, obsessive-compulsive behaviour or withdrawal might lead to such activity while specific obsessions may further encourage scrutiny and aid memory in a certain direction. Heightened and distorted perception may even be influencing his behaviour.

It may be that our brains are more similar in potential than we tend to suppose and that our personalities play a greater part than most of us think in their functioning and achievements.

* * *

This list of personality traits is not, of course, exhaustive but I have tried to describe those which have impinged on my work as a speech and language therapist. The degrees to which children display the traits can be imagined as lying on continua and this makes it appropriate to mingle problematic behaviour with the more commonplace throughout this book. I hope it will become apparent to the reader that serious learning and behavioural difficulties can arise from pronounced manifestations of some traits.

Sometimes a mother with a large family will come to the clinic. She herself might admit to being a very ardent checker of locked doors and pans on stoves, and she routinely rises early to clean spotless items. One son is obsessional, another is hyperactive, a third child has violent tempers, and a young daughter is "very nervous". Between them they exhibit a whole host of the personality traits which I have been describing, yet they are all quite different children. Some of the traits are shared but others are unique to a particular child. Often a child displays such a mixture of traits that one label seems no more appropriate than another.

It perhaps ought to be stressed that compulsive behaviour and quite intense fear are not uncommon in infancy and childhood. Their prevalence should not, however, make us complacent. Better acknowledgement of the particular personality traits of a child and an improved understanding of them should certainly help us to understand him and his anxiety levels better and then our attitude and responses to him can only be improved, whether we are involved as a professional or as a parent.

The following chapter describes the manner in which tension or anxiety may affect speech and language and includes a variety of case studies which illustrate ways in which the various personality traits combine and affect children.

CHAPTER FOUR

SPEECH AND LANGUAGE DIFFICULTIES AS TRAITS

It is the ability to speak and use language which most distinguishes human beings from other species. These skills are the means by which we try to communicate feelings and ideas which cannot be adequately expressed by gesture and facial expressions. We think, speak, read and write using words or symbols and we listen and understand others through language, too. Obviously, communication skills are of enormous importance to individuals and to society as a whole.

Speech and language therapists and linguists never cease to be amazed by the cleverness of young children. By the age of five they are generally using complex sentences. Rather than merely repeat sentence constructions which they have heard others use, children create their own sentences and often delight us with them. They may make a few grammatical errors here and there but that is only to be expected. And it should not surprise us if their speech is not totally clear by the age of five; it is astonishing what they are achieving with their tongues, lips and larynxes, too.

Some speech sounds give children a little more trouble than others. For example, *r* causes more difficulty because it is the only sound for which we need to curl back our tongue. *Sh* and *ch* frequently come late, as does putting *s* with other consonants, as in *spoon, stick, skip, smoke, swing, slip and snow.*

RESISTANCE TO CHANGE AND ADHERENCE TO RULES

In Chapter Three some consideration was given to a common trait which revolves around rituals, routines and a liking for sameness and order. This trait can influence the development of speech and language in a variety of ways. Many children come to a speech and language clinic, are helped to make sounds they are not producing, given practice, are successful and then discharged from the clinic. But others may not respond in this desirable way.

They may not try, for instance, perhaps in order to avoid failure; they might employ demand avoidance strategies; they may find it difficult to break their usual pattern of expression; they may have a need to retain infantile ways, or they may be rather switched off and lack motivation to improve their 'self'. But sometimes they are resistant to change or to the new. A child may, for example, become very attached to a lateral *s* – a rather strange sounding *s* made by shaping the tongue so that the air escapes from the sides of the mouth instead of from the front. In spite of having learned to make *s* correctly, in context and with ease, the child may persist with his incorrect version. When one enquires into the children's present and past behaviour, it may be found that they are, or have been, fond of sameness in other matters.

It is indeed sometimes the case that a child who is reluctant to change his speech will perform well enough in the clinic. But there is no carryover of the practice into his world outside the clinic and he realises that he has failed to achieve what is expected of him. He knows and understands what he is doing wrongly, so he will not be confused in reading and writing should he still have the problem when he goes to school. He can appreciate that *lady* is written with an *l*, even though he pronounces it "yady". If gentle encouragement to change his speech fails, this child may be better left in peace until he becomes self-motivated and ready to change of his own accord. Pressurising him may well increase anxiety.

A child's retention of sameness may affect his vocabulary, too. Some children have their own preferred words for things – even words which seem entirely unrelated to the proper ones – and yet they may have no problem with pronunciation whatsoever. A youngster might persist in saying "didi" for *bed*, for example, although he has no difficulty saying "bird" or "head". I have known a child to say a word clearly, clap his hand over his mouth when he realises that he has broken his 'rule' and refuse to say the word correctly again, reverting to his usual expression of it. Occasionally a child will say something like, "You say 'I', me say 'ME'!" or "No, I don't say that word" when he is encouraged to use one which is not in his repertoire. There may be such an antipathy towards a word and so much negative programming in relation to it that, when the child does eventually have the desire or need to use it, he experiences a difficulty in vocalising it.

Vocabulary is further affected when a child adheres strongly to rules of a grammatical nature. Katie, at seven, insisted on saying, "run over *by* purpose" presumably because we can be run over *by* a car, and older children sometimes continue to say "mans" for *men* because we say "hands", "fans", etc., and not "hend" or "fen". This reluctance to change rules may contribute to a child appearing to take everything he hears literally. He makes a firm rule for himself about what a word or statement means in one context and prevents himself from seeing a different meaning of it in another situation. His rules are rigid and he needs patience and gentle help to assist him in bending them; then he will be able to understand language better for practical purposes since he will know what the speaker means rather than the mere words. The English language is variable and a little consideration makes us realise just how frustrating it could be to someone who makes rigid rules for himself. Examples are plentiful but a few are noted below:

We *feel* a dog and we *feel* sick.

We have a holiday or we *take* a holiday. (Where?)

"It's all above me."

"I haven't got a lot on today." (Clothes or activities?)

"Wait a minute." (Meaning "Oh, I've just remembered" or that someone should wait for an indefinite amount of time.)

"Hold on!" (Literally or otherwise?)

"Give me a hand."

"That's funny." (Funny or strange?)

"That's odd." (Strange or an odd number?)

"He fell over himself/backwards to help."

"It's all water under the bridge now."

"He's blinded by science."

No/know.

hear/here.

Cool and cold. (Temperature or unfriendliness?)

When we say indefinite things such as, "We'll see", "Maybe" or "It all depends", we introduce an element of uncertainty which can be most distressing for a child who is worried by inconsistencies and likes firm rules. He might be upset by our saying "You can't go" on one occasion, when we have permitted the activity on another. It would be better to be more explicit and say, "You can't go today because..." We need to make sure that our instructions are complete and properly sequenced; we should not rely on the child understanding any implicit meaning. We might need to say:

"We shall go shopping after lunch if it doesn't rain" rather than "We may go shopping later on."

"Draw another apple like this one" rather than "Can you draw another apple like this?"

"Let's put the knives and forks on the table so they'll be there at dinner time. That's called getting the table ready or laying the table; we lay things on the table" rather than say, "Lay the table."

"Don't move away from here/me because..." rather than "Don't run off."

Obviously the degree to which we have to be precise with our questions and explanations will be related to the extent of the child's adherence to rules and his ability to process the information. Whilst most children accept that many things which adults say are confusing, and gradually and happily absorb new meanings, some children require very precise information. Sonja kept leaving her garden in spite of her mother's instructions. She was told, "You can play in the garden but don't go on the road" or "Don't go to the park." The little five-year-old obeyed her mother; she did not go on the road or to the park but she did leave the garden (keeping to the pavement). The problem was solved when her mother changed the instruction to "Don't leave the garden. You must stay in the garden."

Karl was pedantic about punishment. One day he was sent to his bedroom until tea-time for being naughty. But his mother had a change of heart and went to fetch him before the allotted time. Karl would not leave his room, however; he insisted on staying until tea-time. The rule was not to be broken. It is important to give a reason to the child, explaining why someone considers it permissible to break the particular rule.

A youngster who thinks in a rigid way may need help to transfer his knowledge to new situations and generalise his learning (another possible reason for poor carryover from a clinic or school). There is also the possibility that he will learn set solutions to problems and apply them rigidly. Whatever approach we adopt to teach him, we should remember that the less anxious he is, the more flexible he should become, and the easier it should be for him to connect ideas and learn.

Resistance to Change and Written Errors

A resistance to change may also contribute to errors in writing. Just as a child may have his own way of saying particular words, so he may have his own way of writing them, be it in the form of the handwriting or in the content. A liking for sameness and adherence to rules (perhaps one's own) may lead to grammatical inaccuracies in writing as well as in speech. When these become variable, the child getting a construction right on one occasion, but wrong on another, there are perhaps some ambivalent feelings.

A dislike of change may also encourage a youngster to persist in mumbling or help prevent a child who is withholding his speech from breaking the pattern of his behaviour. It may ensure that a youngster continues to switch off from, and perhaps avoid, situations which are heavily loaded with language.

It is clear that a child's attempts to keep order, sameness or understanding in his world, can produce many problems for him and for those who try to help him.

COMPREHENSION

We have just seen that strong adherence to rules can create difficulties in understanding language. Obviously children who have difficulty attending or who ignore or switch off can have problems understanding, too; indeed, shutting-out behaviour or automatic shutdown of thinking and the resulting poor comprehension may have led to some rigidity in thinking and adherence to rules.

Of course the severity of the comprehension difficulty of a child who switches off will depend upon the extent to which he is switched off and the kind of situations which cause the shutting out, or failure to switch on and engage the brain properly in an activity. So it depends, in turn, on the extent of any conditioning or programmed behaviour. The understanding of a four-year-old who occasionally switches off is likely to be much better than that of a four-year-old who has switched off regularly since birth. And the understanding of a four-year-old who only switches off when he is being instructed is likely to be a lot better than one who is switched off most of the time.

We need to exercise caution, however. Even in an apparently switched off state, a person may have an awareness of the conversation of others. Parents of children who have been diagnosed as having autism will know that it is necessary to be careful what is said in their presence. Donna Williams (1996) finds that unprocessed information can be absorbed and triggered with meaning at a later time. We cannot therefore assume that a shut down child who does not appear to be understanding will not have the information within him. Moreover, a youngster may find it easier to attend with comprehension to conversation which is not addressed to him.

I have already mentioned that a child may seem visually inattentive or uncomprehending. He may misinterpret pictures, see things in bits rather than as a whole, or disregard visual clues or shapes. If he fails to apply logic (perhaps having a difficulty connecting ideas), a picture of a girl looking at herself in a mirror may be described as "a boy and girl in a mirror". It should not surprise us if, having such problems, a youngster has difficulty understanding the written word, this leading to reading and writing problems. On the other hand, there is the child who involves himself with the shapes, patterns and mechanics of reading but not with the meaning of what he reads, so that his reading comprehension falls way below his actual ability to read.

Just as a child may attend to visual detail and patterns but not to their context, meaning and significance, so may bits and patterns of language be attended to or uttered out of context.

It may be that a child's comprehension difficulties include an inability to see things from another person's point of view. Wimmer and Perner's 'Sally and Ann' experiment is sometimes carried out to highlight a failure to appreciate the working or even the presence of another's mind (Wimmer and Perner, 1983). Ann watches Sally put a marble in a bag. Sally goes away. Ann removes the marble from the bag and puts it into a basket. Where is Sally going to look for the marble when she comes back?

Some children who are well over the age of four years do not seem to be aware that Sally does not know what they know. Perhaps we should not assume that they have a specific inborn difficulty in thinking, however. When we find that they have high levels of anxiety (generally masked to a degree) and may be programmed to have restricted thought processes, it should not really surprise us if they only give partial consideration to a situation or problem or attend to just one or two ideas (assuming they have understood the question in the first place). Children with difficulties in this area may seem to have 'tunnel' thinking and to be socially inept. Williams (1996) highlights a protective shutdown response by the brain when confronted with an excess of information. She also refers to partial temporary shutdown when she might process the meaning of what she sees but not the significance.

It is often the case that parents are unaware of the extent to which their child is habitually not properly attending to what is being said. This is because so much of what we say to a child at home is routine – he does not need to listen carefully for he anticipates what his parent is going to say and has become adept at guessing or filling in the details, perhaps making good use of visual cues and clues. Moreover, he may have grown accustomed to paying little attention to a lot of adult conversation, unless it directly affects him in some important way, because in the past at least, it was confusing or hard to follow. Sometimes poor listening is the result of a busy, egocentric mind.

Below are some requests which a parent might try making to a child at home to ascertain the extent to which he is listening and processing information and to encourage good listening and understanding. Some of the requests include details which are less likely to be guessed. Others are designed to see if the child will attend well to a long request with several ideas or details in it, for the odd key word is sometimes all that is attended to, rather than entire phrases or sentences. We do not want the youngster to think he is being tested, so it is important that the parent at least appears to need what has been asked for — he or she must use the comb which he brings, for example.

1. "I think my comb is behind the curtain/photograph. Will you fetch it please?" (Make sure you have placed your comb where he would not normally expect to find it.)

2. "Please bring me your blue coat/red T-shirt/lace-up shoes, etc."

3. "Which of those bags has a hole in it? Will you look to see? I think I saw a hole in one of them."

4. "I think your ball went under the big chair. See if you can find it." (Avoid looking at the chair.)

5. "Put on your coat and then fetch my bag please."

6. "Will you empty this mug (or some other container) into the sink please?" (Plastic one!)

7. "Will you bring me the smallest towel from the bathroom please?"

8. "Put this pencil next to/beside/on top of/with my shopping list on the sideboard please."

9. "Will you put this tube of toothpaste in the bathroom please and bring me down the old one/the other one?"

10. "Are there any dead flowers in the vase? Are any flowers in the vase dead?"

11. "Have I put out/laid too many knives and forks?"

12. "Have I put out/laid enough knives and forks?"

13. "Do we need any more spoons?"

14. "Have a look to see if the mirror in my bedroom is dirty. Tell me whether it needs cleaning."

15. "See if there's (e.g.) a bar of soap and a bottle of shampoo in the shopping bag."

16. "Be a good boy/girl and get a plastic bag out of the drawer/from the table." (Have paper bags there, too.)

RESPONSE TO FORMAL TESTING

Sometimes a child who adheres rigidly to rules or switches off selectively scores highly in a formal test of verbal comprehension, or perhaps in a test of verbal expression. His teacher, however, complains about his poor understanding and use of language in the classroom. He may demonstrate a capacity to understand well on a general, impersonal level but he fails in more subtle, practical (pragmatic) usage of language. The test has not, for example, highlighted his usual need for explicit instructions or his inability to generalise his learning, nor the fact that he may fare better in more structured situations so that school playtimes might be rather stressful for him. A structured test situation is generally less emotionally intrusive for the child, the administrator behaving predictably and writing notes and scores rather than staring at him or cajoling; this factor will favour the youngster who avoids emotional involvement. Similarly, the child who homes in on detail rather than paying attention to the more meaningful whole will fare better in tasks which are not embedded in context but are carried out for their own sake.

On the other hand, the child may underachieve on tests, particularly if he avoids demands or if a switch-off or shutdown leads to an inability to recall information to order or handle more than one idea at a time.

MUMBLING

My case history taking has enabled me to detect a link between anxiety and mumbled or muffled speech. The young child may feel quite ambivalent about speaking – he has a need to talk and a need not to. He can control and vary the clarity of his words by mumbling and perhaps rushing his speech, and hence he can control the degree to which he communicates. Many a time when people have complained that they cannot understand a child, I have completed a speech analysis and found little or nothing at all amiss with his actual ability to say words clearly; he makes sounds correctly and with ease, in the right positions. Such children tend to be referred back to speech and language clinics.

Sometimes simple inattention to clarity can result in a child's speech being rushed and difficult to understand.

MUTISM

It may be that an anxious child will elect not to talk at all. Often he is quite selective in his mutism, talking to some people but not to others, or in some situations but not in others. Perhaps he only speaks through a toy, or in a squeaky voice or different accent or persona. Such controlling behaviour may become heavily conditioned so that even when he really tries hard to break a pattern and speak, nothing comes out. People often suppose then, erroneously, that there is something wrong with his tongue or with his larynx. One mother found her mute child standing alone in front of a mirror, making speech sounds; he stopped this activity as soon as his mother appeared – or was unable to continue on her arrival.

When a child is conditioned to be mute in a selective way, it can be a relatively simple matter to remedy the situation, assuming he is psychologically ready for the change. If, for example, he will speak to his family but not to anyone at playschool, one might bring him and his mother or father together in a quiet room at the playschool. His teacher may well find that if she takes a back seat (figuratively or literally), he will indeed speak to her in his parent's presence, in such a room. The next step would be for the parent to accompany him in a quiet corner of the playschool room until he is able to converse with anyone in the group. In time, the presence of the parent should no longer be necessary.

A nondidactic, undemanding approach may help the mute child over his difficulties. If one were looking at a picture book with him, for example, one might talk about the pictures without asking questions or appearing to expect a response, or perhaps questions could be asked in such a way that the child understands that a reply is not necessarily expected. In this way, negative behaviour is not reinforced.

Since conditioning can result in a mute child finding it difficult to speak, he may be inaccurately labelled dyspraxic.

VOICE

Many physical and allergic conditions can affect vocal quality in children and adults, as may vocal abuse. Occasionally a child grows hoarse after a bout of crying or shouting. If he shouts frequently and talks loudly and incessantly he might even develop nodes or nodules on his vocal cords. It is reasonable to consider the role that tension or anxiety may play in dysphonia in children, as in adults. Margaret Greene states, "There is such a strong anxiety component in the personality structure of these individuals who suffer from vocal abuse that one is led to believe that they (the organic lesions) are akin to psychosomatic disorders." (The Voice and its Disorders, 1989.) Certainly psychosomatic problems are frequently associated with dysphonia, as speech and language therapists working in a voice clinic are well aware.

We have already considered mutism in the child where, as a result of psychological influences, it can sometimes seem physically difficult to develop speech or speak in certain situations. It is not uncommon for an anxious adult to temporarily lose his voice and show a weakness or propensity for troubles in the vocal area, and I am reminded of a teenager with anorexia nervosa who came to see me because her voice had suddenly disappeared.

Anxiety can make a child's voice and intonation somewhat idiosyncratic. Sometimes he chooses to speak through a character, rather than himself, or he may have a preference for a certain tone or rhythm. He may speak with an infantile or high-pitched voice. He may have difficulty understanding, and hence using, intonation.

RETENTION OF INFANTILE BEHAVIOUR

A young child may not be ready, emotionally, to develop speech and language. If he does speak, he might grunt or use only a very simple sound system or one that renders him largely unintelligible to all, except perhaps his close family. His speech may even take the form of jargon (gibberish) interspersed with an occasional clear word. Sometimes jargon only occurs at moments of extra tension or excitement, or it arises routinely (possibly ritualistically) at certain times of the day.

A child who has ventured forth with his speech and toilet training may, upon feeling anxious, return to former ways or fail to make further progress for a while. Parents often say that their infant began to speak but suddenly stopped.

OBSESSIONAL SPEECH

We have already considered the youngster who talks continually on a subject with which he is obsessed. There is also the child who insists that his mother repeats back what he has just said in exactly the same way each time – an obsessional (or compulsive) and ritualistic type of behaviour. Sometimes he asks questions repetitively and likes to receive the same answer each time. The child appears to derive satisfaction from hearing the familiar pattern of speech unfold, whether the repetitions are his own or others'.

Some children show a compulsion for talking. When such a child is denied an audience or someone to answer his questions, he may talk to himself. He may feel so compelled to hear often heard, predictable speech, that the episodes of talking to himself involve reliving typical conversations. Sometimes these have a rather negative content, perhaps even revolving around others' correction of his behaviour, involving sentences such as "Now we don't want to be silly, do we?" The child may repeatedly carry out an action for which he expects to receive predictable correction. If this correction is not forthcoming, he may pester the adult for it or supply it himself – "You can't go up there because you'll fall?...Because you'll get dirty?...You can go later?" Some consideration may help us to distinguish between the child who is genuinely seeking an answer and the youngster who is perhaps obsessed with hearing orderly, familiar speech.

ORGANISATION OF LANGUAGE

A somewhat switched off or anxious child may find his thoughts sluggish or difficult to organise or connect. This can lead him to give confused or "I don't know" answers. Names may be less well recalled (or even lose their meaning) and ideas may be difficult to sequence; the ensuing loss of confidence worsens the situation. Whilst the youngster may be rather silent and unforthcoming, he is sometimes prone to giving immediate, impulsive, and perhaps irrelevant responses – maybe triggered by something which someone has said. So unless this unfortunate young person is bound by ritual or resorts to mimicry, he may have poorly organised thoughts, speak in poorly organised sentences and exhibit quite disorganised behaviour. He may find himself regularly saying or writing things in the wrong order or he may miss out or unnecessarily repeat words when he is speaking or writing. Such a person may prefer to learn a block of text which he can reproduce verbatim in an examination, rather than try to organise his thoughts.

Although a depressed or shut down child may have sluggish thoughts and experience the problems outlined above, he might at other times find his head buzzing with thoughts which seem too numerous and erratic to cope with. A 'hyped up', alert state of mind may, however, aid some people's verbal or literary performance. It is interesting that many great poets and comedians are, or have been, people who are prone to depression and mania. Many of us will know very witty people who have unusually gloomy downsides.

TYPICAL SPEECH OF MANY ANXIOUS CHILDREN

The young child who is referred to a speech and language clinic for his delayed speech and language is indeed frequently a rather anxious and fearful child. If he is speaking in sentences, he may habitually omit sub-key words, such as auxiliary verbs and the little words such as 'to', 'the' and 'a'. He may pay scant attention to pronouns and prepositions; personal pronouns might not be used or may be used incorrectly, particularly if he withdraws or resists change. His use of past and future tenses may be poor. His sentences might be muddled – with him saying things in the wrong order and his speech is often mumbled and indistinct. He may not ask questions (which tend to necessitate involvement as well as a connection of ideas), in particular failing to use the word 'why'. (Some children who withdraw pose questions in the form of statements, whilst others may make statements in the form of questions.) His vocabulary may be restricted, idiosyncratic and sometimes applied inappropriately (particularly when influenced by experiential associations or when triggered). He may give inappropriate answers to questions, or answers to ones he expects to be asked. He may have difficulty being specific.

STAMMERING

The words stammering and stuttering are synonymous. The onset of initial symptoms of stammering can sometimes be seen to coincide with stressful events in a young child's life. The symptoms may first occur when he is afraid, shocked, bereaved, ill or uncertain. They can result, for example, from a child worrying about forgetting his address, having been told at his playgroup to remember it. Or they can arise because a child is anxious about moving to another class. I have found that children who stammer have, or have had, personality traits related to anxiety or tension.

Stammering is habitual, conditioned, repetitive and spasmodic behaviour, reminiscent of tics and their compulsive qualities. A variety of theories exist to explain it. My own view is that it develops from compulsive behaviour (Sims, 1997). It begins with simple repetitions of sounds and syllables which, I hypothesise, become habitual and compulsive in some children. I suggest that when the child attempts to pass on to the next syllable or word, he is at the same time programmed or 'needing' to continue the compulsive repetitions – his brain is receiving conflicting messages. We therefore have a block (when nothing comes out) and then a struggle. The behaviour becomes conditioned to (or triggered by) certain feelings or circumstances and the patterns of stammering reinforce themselves.

Some adults who stammer have retained compulsive feelings and feel an urge or need to do it in spite of wishing to be rid of the affliction and seeking help to this end. The release of tension after each struggle can be addictive. In such cases the stammer would not be being maintained by conditioning alone.

The earlier stammering behaviour is properly attended to, the better it is for the child. Obviously, a thorough case history and discussion with a parent can give us an appreciation of the child's levels of tension and the degree to which they are being sustained by removable environmental factors, but he may also benefit from the Lidcombe Programme. This originates from Australia and is being promoted by Professor Mark Onslow, an Australian researcher (Onslow, O'Brian and Harrison, 1997). It includes praising the child for fluent speech and sometimes correcting repetitions in a particular and sensitive manner. The programme is adapted to suit the specific needs of a child but he always receives valuable special attention and positive support from his parents. Correcting children who are very sensitive to criticism can be harmful but if the programme is sensitively and appropriately implemented under the guidance of a speech and language therapist it can inhibit the repetitions.

It is, of course, a common and quite natural thing for young children to repeat words and syllables a little as they learn to express themselves. In most cases the behaviour does not develop into a stammer. It is, nevertheless, better to have an understanding of the feelings and mechanisms behind stammering if we are to prevent it. A thorough understanding of the youngster's stage of dysfluency, his feelings and his behaviour is of importance in determining our particular approach to his problem.

It is indeed my opinion that stammering behaviour originates in commonplace childhood anxiety or tension which is often within normal limits – it is simply the case that habitually repeating words and syllables has more scope for complications than do most other personality traits.

CLUTTERING

Cluttering is very rushed, poorly articulated speech. It resembles stammering in that it becomes difficult for the child to control and breathing patterns are disturbed, but there is no blocking or prolonging of sounds and the child does not appear to struggle with his words. In my experience, children who clutter their speech have or have had tension or anxiety-related personality traits.

Occasionally breathing patterns are habitually disturbed during speech with a frequent noisy intake of air (in spite of there being no physical abnormality), yet the speech is not cluttered or stammered.

DYSPRAXIA OF SPEECH

Dyspraxia of speech is a term frequently used to describe the difficulty some children have in articulating, with intent, sounds and words which they are able to articulate in theory. (They can demonstrate a physical ability to make the appropriate sounds.) The youngsters generally exhibit anxiety-related traits or have exhibited them in the past. The dyspraxia can therefore be associated with slow, delayed or disconnected thinking, poor retrieval of the sound of words or their parts, and with incorrect programming.

These children may practise away to no avail. If a method is not working it is generally advisable to change it. When one tries to help such a child, the tendency is to break down the word into its parts, starting at the beginning. This is, of course, how the child has always attempted to say the word, and he consequently associates the approach with failure and continues to make errors. It is, therefore, far more productive to begin with the end of the word. Let us suppose that we are trying to help the child to say "curtain". We could ask him to say the word as follows:

tain
cur
tain (stress this)
curtain (slowly)

or for the word 'club':

lub
c
lub
club

And if he is ready to attempt a longer word, such as 'ordinary':

ary
inary
*din*ary
or–dinary
ordinary

One will find that this method usually helps the youngster to attend properly to the sound of the words and their parts. He will, however, probably need daily practice in order to supplant his customary ways of saying them.

***

It has been my intention in this chapter to associate some speech and language difficulties with personality traits and not to comment on all possible problems concerning speech and language, such as those which may result from brain damage, cleft palate or a hearing loss.

Tension or anxiety appears to play a very significant part in bringing about difficulties to which I have been referring. That there may often be a strong inherent factor in anxiety or tension is suggested by the prevalence of traits among infants with loving, caring and capable parents, in circumstances which do not appear untoward – traits which frequently show soon after birth. There may be in some of these cases, of course, relevant familial factors and other environmental influences of which I am unaware. Although such influences are of great import in every case, the subject of origin of anxiety is too vast to receive in this book the attention it merits. It is the effects of anxiety and its association with problems, rather than its origins, to which I should chiefly like to draw the reader's attention.

Let us now see how tension or anxiety has affected the speech of some children. I have not included any cases where real neglect or ill-treatment of a child was known or suspected. Sometimes parents have their own problems of depression, switching off, etc. It may be that the children have inherited a predisposition for excess anxiety from such parents or have been affected by stress hormones in the womb (see p.24) but they may be reacting to stress created by a parent's personal difficulties.

Jude

Jude was a "very good" infant until the age of two. He is now nearly five. He is a most anxious little boy. He is a poor sleeper and is still in nappies at night. He will not get into a bed of his own; he sleeps with his parents and will only sleep when they are with him and if the light is left on. He still falls over a lot and walks into things. He is poor at judging the amount of physical force required to do something. Although frightened by traffic, he walks out in front of cars. Noises can terrify him, even moderately loud banging in a building; he is frightened by the wind. Jude is fond of routine and does not like change. He insists on wearing the same things, and he cries if the grass is cut. During tempers his body goes rigid and he vomits. He rocks and bites himself. Being rather egocentric, he does not mix well with other children, and he copies bad behaviour without understanding it. He is obsessed with videos, and watches the same thing over and over again, particularly cartoons. He will often do things of his own accord but not if asked to do them, and he might change his activity if demands are made on him. He follows his mother about the house. He has a very good memory and is clever at doing puzzles. He can sit and concentrate but, generally in the clinic, he prefers to go off to play.

When Jude was first seen for a speech and language assessment his speech was clear but he repeated most of what his mother said and there was no proper two-way conversation. His understanding was poor and his answers to questions were inappropriate. He did not ask questions himself.

I shall now describe Jude's reaction when he was encouraged to ask questions. I had decided to try some 'Wh' questions – *Where? Why? What?* and *Who?* To this end, I took out an exercise book and drew a picture of a pig behind a tree. I whispered, "Does Mummy know where the pig is? Say, 'Where's the pig, Mummy?'" At this suggestion Jude became more stressed than usual and developed a panic reaction. He looked quite petrified and took deep breaths. I quickly turned the page and took time to draw another, different picture, again gently encouraging a 'Wh' question. This elicited a similar response to my initial picture but I continued to proceed slowly in this manner through the book. Gradually Jude became more calm, realising that he was under no pressure to ask a question. He reached a point where he could indeed ask his mother the question, to their mutual delight. He was then able to return to the beginning of the book and ask her all the questions. When they came back to the clinic a week later his mother said that he had been asking questions every day.

What can we deduce from this episode? Had Jude initially not asked questions because that would have involved him too much in his environment? I think there are good grounds, when his personality traits are taken into consideration, for believing this to be a strong possibility. There are, too, ample reasons for considering that he might find it difficult to break a rule. His panic reactions suggest a high level of anxiety and some conditioning of behaviour. Quite obviously, this is a child who must be properly understood by all who seek to help him if serious harm to his well-being is to be avoided.

Fay

Fay's father learned to read at an early age – before he went to school. But he was considered an enigmatic child and he spent many of his school hours in remedial classes. His mother complained of him switching off.

Fay is an underweight four-year-old; she has always eaten very little and only likes certain foods, often insisting on the same brands. She has intense tempers, avoids demands and has switched off since her infancy. She is prone to colds and ear infections. She cannot name colours, but she can sort pieces of wool according to their hues. She plays imaginatively now; she used to spend hours just sitting on her tricycle. Fay's parents understand her reticence. They know she is happy in her restricted world and indeed, she is developing nicely within it, and has begun to broaden it. She will chatter away these days. In spite of having good imitative ability, her speech is mostly unintelligible and includes some jargon, but it is encouraging that all new words added to her vocabulary are now said clearly. There is still a strong resistance to changing her speech (she is visibly upset when a 'forbidden', correct word escapes her lips), but there are signs that she is breaking free of some of her programming and she seems less 'selfish' than before.

Despite plenty of reasons for optimism, there is the threat of pressure looming large, for Fay is expected to start school soon and everyone has begun to wonder how she, and her teacher, will cope.

Anna and Charlotte

Anna and Charlotte are four-year-old genetically identical twins. Both switched off on their visit to my clinic. Although they can do some puzzles at their nursery and home, they had little success with even the most simple of those which I gave them. They attempted mine but did not involve themselves properly with any task. They both have a history of screaming and sitting inertly and they display no proper sense of danger. They suffer from eczema.

The twins have indistinct speech and they tend to share their own particular words for things. Sometimes they echo repetitively what they have heard others say. Charlotte likes to be the same as her sister. She has even tried to copy a stammer which Anna has acquired, but Anna will not permit it, insisting that only she is allowed to do it.

It is interesting that Anna seems to be the more serious of the two and that Charlotte appears to be less anxious, perhaps because she is leaning on and generally taking her cue from her sister. Maybe Anna's anxiety is increased by Charlotte's dependence on her.

Kate

Kate is approaching four. She was an unusually quiet and good baby but that has all changed. Now she has daily outbursts of temper when she can be aggressive and self-abusive. She bites herself and others, bangs her head against the wall and pulls her hair. She never crawled, still dribbles, and does not react to pain; nor does she show an appropriate awareness of danger. She appears not to moderate the amount of physical force she uses so that cuddles from her actually hurt the recipient. She does not respond to physical punishment but she habitually smacks her own bottom after doing something she would normally be smacked for doing. She is not facially expressive, tending to have rather a fixed stare.

Being frequently terrified by noise, Kate might bury her head among the sofa cushions if she hears a helicopter or even the vacuum cleaner. And she is very anxious in a new room or building. She is a poor sleeper, and her mother has to stay with her until she falls asleep. Even so, she gets out of her own bed and climbs in with her parents every night.

Kate always eats the same food or sweets and insists on ending each meal with a bowl of cereal. Although she is a fussy eater she will eat enormous quantities of foods for which she has a liking. She has a most adverse reaction to a change in cutlery, cup or plate. She is extremely stubborn.

There are plenty of rituals in Kate's life. These revolve around speech, kisses, collecting objects and the daily routine. She repeatedly throws balls down the road so that she can enjoy the ritual of someone running to fetch them. She is obsessive about tunes and songs and about keeping in sight of her mother. She will not allow her parents to give her brothers and sisters any attention. She fiddles with things and flits from one activity to another. Nothing is concentrated on for long, her anxiety about keeping her mother in view probably being a contributory factor. She switches off from her surroundings, avoids demands, and is indifferent to praise.

These are just some of Kate's personality traits. And how do they affect her language? Firstly, she requires very clear and precise instructions or statements before she can understand, and she reacts badly in uncertain situations. She has difficulty understanding time sequences, so that yesterday and tomorrow have no meaning for her. She is often silent, even refusing to talk. She will not use the word 'I', preferring 'me' and her naming is frequently inaccurate or imprecise – she called a basket a "box", a horse a "cow", and a flower a "tree", for example. One cannot hold a proper two-way conversation with Kate and she puts on a deep, husky voice. Her sentences are suggestive of a much younger child, her speech is unclear, and she never answers questions. She does, however, ask 'What' and 'Where' questions but these are used repetitively, as she constantly asks her mother the same thing. A road sign was removed from her street. Three months later it was still part of Kate's routine to ask her mother where it was; it is probable that she liked hearing the same reply.

I think we can predict that Kate will have some learning problems in the classroom.

Bruce

Bruce's language sounds pedantic – and has always, at least superficially, seemed too mature for his years. He is thirteen now, but for many years he has been copying adults in what they say and how they say it; his sense of identity is poor. In the manner of his teacher, he might address fellow pupils with, "I do think it would be better if you were to..." or "Now, I should like you all to be silent and give me your full attention, please." His apparent command of the English language belies an inability to understand its subtleties and to use it well practically, with unfortunate social consequences. Indeed, people find him odd. He has difficulty comprehending humour or sarcasm, although he might repeat a simple joke he has heard, ad nauseam. He bores people by telling them what they already know, for their feelings and their knowledge are not considered – consideration for others appears to be shut out from his world, a world in which order must take precedence. Ironically, he seems disorganised in the classroom, where rituals, routine and obsessions are of greater importance to him than furthering his education. He seeks to restrict and contain his world, not to have it broadened.

Bruce adheres strongly to rules and facts. He has always amazed people with his knowledge of cars, registration numbers, or anything else that interests him but at the same time puzzles them with his laborious handwriting and poor comprehension of what he has read. He has excellent skills in mental arithmetic but is unable to do mathematical problems which involve context and require flexibility of thinking, and he is not able to empathise in history lessons, preferring charts and dates which can be memorised as pure fact.

This young lad is prone to epileptic fits. He may become angry and even a little violent when his school routine is changed – and sometimes it is the small alterations which upset him most. He has always become distressed when he has had to join a noisy, overcrowded classroom. Anxiety can keep him awake at night.

Bruce sometimes binges on a particular food, carries the same carrier bag around with him, and still wears his warm jacket during the summer months. He plays the French horn in an orchestra. During rehearsal breaks he mentally devours the orchestral score; he times the breaks to the last second and becomes most upset if everyone does not resume practice at the appointed moment.

Bruce's peers use him for their amusement. It did not take long for them to discover that he would sometimes do naughty things if they told him to do them, for although he tends to abide by rules, he has not properly developed a conscience nor an entirely appropriate idea of right and wrong. He is unable to discriminate between people laughing with him and people laughing at him. One boy created laughs by pulling down his trousers in the games changing room. After this, Bruce pulled down his trousers in the classroom – he got the laughs (except from his teacher), but could not see that the laughter was of a different nature. He has never been good at interpreting facial expressions – winks and meaningful eye movements have held no meaning for him, for example. His switching off has led people to suspect deafness; in fact, he now affects deafness, which adds somewhat to the confusion.

Bruce's biggest problem seems to be anxiety and the programmed and ritualistic responses that anxiety has created for him.

Yatish

Yatish is progressing quite well at school. Sometimes he seems very cheerful but he may suddenly start crying for no obvious reason. He is an eight-year-old who worries a great deal about things and he clutters his speech – he rushes through what he is trying to say, with disturbed breath patterns, omitting words or parts of them and generally mispronouncing many words. He began to develop a habit of throat clearing which threatened to become a tic. Fortunately Yatish became less anxious about things at school, his speech improved, and a tic did not develop.

Michael

Except with speech, Michael was forward as a baby and toddler. He is a three and a half-year-old ardent thumb-sucker who squeals for no apparent reason. He suffers from nasal congestion, the cause of which has not been established. He overreacts and has explosive temper tantrums in which he bites himself and hits his mother. He is very stubborn and impatient. He frequently refuses to walk. He fidgets and fiddles with things but does not play for long, and his play is never imaginative. He is often bored in spite of all attempts to occupy him. He is independent at playgroup, 'doing his own thing', regardless of what everyone else is doing; he is somewhat egocentric. He displays no sense of danger and his mother is sure he would go off with anyone. He is a fussy eater who may gorge on a food he favours, and he likes to collect labels and bits of paper. Sometimes he ignores people and looks blank.

Michael babbled but he did not say any words until he was two years old. Even when he did start to talk he added to his vocabulary only very slowly. At three and a half his speech is muffled and mumbled, although he can speak clearly. His sentences are very short and his understanding is rather poor. He will ask questions but they always seem to be the same ones. He is often visually erratic, giving puzzles and pictures no more than a cursory glance and the television holds no interest for him.

If Michael is typical, his tempers will gradually decrease, his speech will blossom, and his comprehension will improve as his interest in the world overrides his reticence concerning it. But we should be alerted to his above average degree of anxiety and take note of his present poor ability to attend and his leaning towards hyperactivity.

Joe

Joe's language development is well ahead of his four and a half years. His basic understanding is better than that of most children his age and he uses wonderfully complex sentences. So why was a speech and language therapist asked to see him? He was referred because there were one or two speech sounds which he did not say. On investigation it appeared that Joe was a rather anxious little boy and that his speech delay might be related to a resistance to change.

Joe had been a very good baby who did not crawl. He seems a little clumsy with a stamping, heavy kind of walk. He has an excellent memory for past events; it seems that he even remembers being born. He is anxious when he is in new situations and is easily frightened by noise – the wind or a brass band, for example. He is terrified by dogs and horses and is most cautious of traffic. He overreacts to rather trivial things and can be extremely stubborn. He will not stay in his own bed, ever since he had a bad dream. He likes everything to be in its proper place; he likes the furniture in the clinic to be positioned in the same way on each of his visits and he will not leave the room without putting away toys, etc. He needs to know in advance what is going to happen the next day. He likes the same foods.

Joe generally listens to people's conversations for it seems he is desperate to know all about this rather frightening planet. He asks lots of questions and demands full, precise explanations. One can hold good two-way conversations with him.

Here we have an example of anxiety actually assisting a child's development in certain areas. But we must understand Joe's precocity if we are to properly help him, and be aware that it might set him aside from his peers.

Peter

Peter has always had loose bowels and hospital investigations have not established an organic cause. He is faddy about his food and although he is now almost six, he looks rather like a delicate four-year-old. Peter goes rigid when he is in a temper and may even be sick or have a convulsion. He wakes up very early in the morning and is prone to nightmares. He has to kiss his sister goodbye every day and take the 'proper' route to places. He walks with a lilt, has a spiky finger action and a squint (strabismus). He is apt to fall off a pony he rides through "forgetting" to hold onto the reins, or holding them too limply in an absent manner.

Peter can seem rather switched off and he employs avoidance strategies, such as giggling and changing the subject. He displays a short attention span and he takes a very long time to put on even a few items of clothing. His parents and his teachers have sometimes to say things in two or three different ways to him before he properly understands. He persists in using his own particular words, which often leads to inaccurate grammar, and he tends not to ask questions. He mispronounces a few words and seems reluctant to change his speech patterns but he practises with complete success in the clinic.

Peter's eight-year-old sister, in spite of constant correction by her mother, has retained one or two immaturities of speech. She is even-tempered but not at all fond of change and a poor sleeper. She is a conscientious pupil who is progressing nicely at school; Peter has learning difficulties. The children's mother complains that their father never takes on any responsibilities – but he does worry unnecessarily about his health.

Robin

There was very little wrong with five-year-old Robin's speech. Although he was shy and subdued when he first came to the clinic, he practised hard to correct the few sounds he did not use, with excellent results, both inside and outside the clinic. He has a liking for exactness and orderliness and is determined to succeed in everything he does. Although he was not the most agile in the school's gym room, he became a splendid little worker in the classroom and soon had a reading and spelling age well beyond his years. It took Robin some time to decide which hand to use for writing; he settled for the left but he displays some general ambidexterity. In his early years he had become very attached to his personal possessions and would not see them removed or replaced by new ones – he could seem very stubborn.

Robin is another example of a child whose progress is being assisted by a little extra anxiety. He confronts new tasks and situations with determination. Having never switched off academically, he is able to cope with his self-imposed pressure, at least at the present time.

Rowena

Rowena is nine. She has a stammer, and has been diagnosed as dyslexic. She speaks quietly through lips which are barely opened, and she keeps her tongue forward in her mouth (despite having a normal dental bite). She has eczema and her sister suffers from asthma. Rowena has always awoken in the early hours of the morning and not gone back to sleep again. She chews her nails. She has a need to urinate more frequently than is usual and the cause of this has not been established.

David

David had no marked tension or anxiety-related traits. When he was aged three his family moved house and his father left home temporarily. It was at this time that his speech regressed and jargon came to the fore, although he was capable of speaking clearly.

***

This is just a sample of the common problems which are encountered in a speech and language clinic. Often, after a very busy day, I find that most of the children whom I have seen have come as a result of difficulties which stem from traits associated with tension or anxiety. I know that a lot of the problems will be resolved, but I acknowledge the importance of our learning about the child from them – to help him in his passage through school and into adulthood, and in some cases to perhaps even prevent mental illness.

In order to demonstrate the prevalence of anxiety-related personality traits and their association with developmental difficulties, I have summarised, in the following table, some traits and problems experienced by twelve children who were seen in order of referral; no selection was made.

Child's age & language problem	Fearfulness/ sensitivity	Repetitive behaviour	Switching off/ avoidance/poor attention	Other
2 yr 9 mth Slow speech and language development		Likes mother to say the same things		Exacting and stubborn
3 yr 2 mth Arrested development of speech and language	Cries when left at playschool; reticent			Some regression in development
3 yr 1 mth Jargon; poor comprehension; word and sound repetitions	Cries out for mother during night; poor sleeper	Rituals; repetitive questioning	May switch off and avoid	Day-time soiling; severe tantrums; fervent dummy sucking; fussy eating
6 yr 2 mth Delayed language	Very sensitive to criticism; frightened to go upstairs at night		Tends not to listen well when instructed; opts out	Marked tempers
3 yr 11 mth Hurried speech; lateralisation of sounds; use of silly voice; inappropriate word usage			Short attention span and distractible but can also seem preoccupied	Excitability; clumsiness; unusually large appetite
3 yr 2 mth Single words only – when willing	Sensitive to criticism and clingy	Orderly and very fussy; resistant to change; repeats words (not as in stammering)	Ignores people	Undetermined handedness; heightened reaction to sounds; occasional rocking
6 yr 6 mth Dysfluency; difficulty organising language	Frightened of noises; very sensitive; anxious questioning	Repetitive questioning	Rather poor eye contact and involvement	Bed-wetting; poor awareness of danger; slow and poor dressing

Child's age & language problem	Fearfulness/ sensitivity	Repetitive behaviour	Switching off/ avoidance/poor attention	Other
2 yr 4 mth No speech but has begun to make noises	Regularly terrified; nightmares; poor sleeper		Rather aloof; not very responsive	Outbursts of screaming; eczema; left-handed
5 yr 6 mth Delayed language; learning problems at school		Repetitive 'naughty' behaviour and some rigidity in thinking	May avoid	Egocentricity and some lack of empathy
4 yr 0 mth Delayed language; selective mutism; some intentional lack of clarity	Calls out for mother during night; anxious questioning	Repetitive speech and some ritualistic behaviour	"Trance-like" switching off; avoidance	Marked tantrums; unusually observant; walks about holding comforter; fussy eater; left-handed
10 yr 0 mth Verbal comprehension and expressive difficulties; literacy and memory problems	Very reticent; panic attacks; night-time anxieties			Fidgety and restless; ?depression
6 yr 7 mth Literacy problems; disordered language	Very sensitive to criticism		"Dreams"	Notes tiny changes to surroundings; asks questions about the day's agenda; bed-wetting; clumsiness; keen thumb-sucking

CHAPTER FIVE

DIFFICULT BEHAVIOUR – APPLYING KNOWLEDGE GAINED FROM AN ENQUIRY INTO PERSONALITY TRAITS

It is to be expected that a child's speech and language will be influenced by the behaviour, beliefs, values and expectations of those around him and by events which affect him, for good or ill, and so too will be his general behaviour. Inherent predisposition towards anxiety must also be a contributory factor. Whatever might be the cause of or provocation for his anxiety, were it not for its prevalence, we should often see a quite different child. Whilst tension or anxiety might encourage conscientiousness, diligence and well-conducted behaviour, it can also result in difficult conduct in some children. Let us consider some ways in which its manifestations through personality traits might create behavioural problems.

AGGRESSION

Tension is commonly released in the form of anger. The angry person may find himself wanting to hit out at things, and as we have already seen, people may direct aggression towards themselves. Sometimes a child controls his anger and aggressive feelings at school but feels compelled to express them immediately after school. Similarly, a young child may learn to control his aggression with people outside the family but direct it at those closest to him.

The Case of Dominic

Dominic was a lethargic baby. He did not walk until he was two years old, was clumsy, asked questions repetitively, and kept echoing back what people said. He is now eight but he still switches off and he rocks at times. He has difficulty sleeping, resists change and has very bad tempers. He tells lies with no sign of a conscience and he does not relate well to other children, preferring the company of adults. Dominic's mother says that he would go off with anyone. He has learning difficulties.

Dominic has a compulsion to hit other children. He is constantly picking fights with them. He will even go up to a group of much older boys who may be strangers to him, and hit them. He knows he will be hit back but this is exactly what he wants; it seems to be part of a ritual.

Whilst Dominic's aggressive behaviour may have begun with feelings of anger and frustration, it now appears to be sustained by obsessive-compulsive activity.

DEFIANCE

While children may be defiant for a variety of reasons, the case of Owen shows how anxiety might cause obstinate defiance.

Owen is a three-year-old with several rituals and a few other signs of heightened anxiety. His mother is concerned that he is very defiant; she finds his deliberate disobedience most distressing.

Owen, like Dominic, is driven by a need to obtain a desired effect. His mother tells him not to do something. He disobeys. She tells him off, and as he continues with his disobedience she goes through various stages of re-proof and anger. It is not until she has become distraught that he is completely satisfied. It would seem that he does not react this way because he is simply always wanting to upset his mother or command her attention (although the latter may be an influencing factor). It appears rather that he enjoys seeing and hearing, and feels compelled to see and hear a familiar pattern of events and utterances unfold.

Many little children seem to delight in spending their day doing or saying one naughty thing after another. This behaviour and the reactions it brings provides and feeds a nice, familiar, repetitive daily pattern for them – a pattern which we help to maintain by our repetitive and manipulable responses. I have found that if one ignores such behaviour as far as possible and that if obliged to respond, the matter is dealt with calmly, in a matter-of-fact manner with minimal or no verbal response, the repetitive naughtiness begins to diminish. One might remove the child physically but calmly from a situation, perhaps talking quietly of some other matter. There is likely to be an initial period when the youngster reacts with more persistent mischief and with a degree of anger to the unfamiliar responses from the adult, but this will not last.

Full consideration of environmental effects on behaviour is well beyond the scope of this book. Nevertheless, it may not be difficult to see a factor which increases anxiety and repetitive behaviour and provokes the defiance. Sometimes, for example, a mother's working arrangements may be suspect, particularly if the hours, days or weeks which she works vary and the child cannot define a structure or routine. Moreover, if a mother has feelings of guilt about neglecting her child to go out to work, she may treat him rather indulgently at times while responding with anger at other times; he will suffer from the inconsistency and lack of parental control, his security being undermined.

ANTI-SOCIAL BEHAVIOUR

Rigid and obsessive-compulsive behaviour (including some avoidance) can be of an anti-social nature, and we have already seen that being partially switched off may affect the development of a conscience and empathy. Shutting out information or only partially processing it restricts a child's understanding and can result in him performing some very strange acts; he may not be able to appreciate the significance of his actions. He may urinate in the bath, set light to the curtains, take what does not belong to him, imitate undesirable behaviour of others and exhibit a degree of selfishness, spite and rudeness which quite shocks people. He may appear to listen to one's correction and advice and seem to agree with it, but his poor sense of responsibility, perhaps coupled with poor ability to generalise his learning, leads him into trouble again.

Occasionally anxious children seem to have a hatred for a sibling. This might result from a very strong attachment to a parent or belongings or from fears or suspicions. Sometimes a child is most distressed by a baby sibling's crying and social facial expressions – and wants him to be removed.

***

When a youngster is obviously affected by some condition, as in the more severe cases of autism, we find it easy to make allowances for his behaviour. When he appears normal except for some difficult behaviour, we perhaps have a tendency to respond inappropriately. An increased understanding must be fundamental to any improvement in this situation; it is necessary to give thought to the present and past personality traits of the child.

It is likely that inherent predisposition towards anxiety, anxiety provoking experiences and the ability of a parent to adapt to and cope with these factors all play their part and problems may be compounded if a parent has similar difficulties to the child's. He, too, may be quite disorganised, for example, finding it extremely difficult to work through his child's learning or behavioural problems or even to remember an appointment with a professional who offers help, despite being genuinely concerned for his offspring. Unfortunately this is sometimes the situation. Even more unfortunately there are some cases, perhaps inevitably, where both parents appear to display anxiety related problems akin to those of their child. Looking on the plus side, however, a parent who shares his child's difficulties can often identify and sympathise with the youngster's fearfulness or other traits.

When considering the reasons for children's conditions and behaviour there is a tendency to accept the most obvious, or the ones on the lips of others. A child known to me is believed to have learning difficulties as a result of being flung against a wall by an aggressive parent. Whilst the adult's action is lamentable, might not the child's anxiety, problematic behaviour and early learning difficulties have driven his parent to violence, especially if the parent himself is a naturally anxious or tense person (who may have passed on such traits to his child)? And should it not be considered that a marriage may have broken up partly as the result of a child's difficult behaviour rather than the break up be assumed the major cause of his difficulties? Circumstances may be highly complex but our thinking could profit by taking a child's early personality traits as its starting point.

CHAPTER SIX

DYSLEXIA AND PERSONALITY TRAITS

The British Dyslexia Association defines dyslexia as: *"Organising or learning difficulties affecting language, fine co-ordination skills and working memory skills. It is independent of overall ability and conventional teaching. When untreated, there are significant limitations in the development of specific aspects of speech, reading, spelling, writing and sometimes numeracy – which may lead to secondary behavioural problems – although other areas of ability are unaffected."*

What causes dyslexia? It is widely believed that a child who has been diagnosed dyslexic is unfortunate enough to have inherited a specific deficiency of the brain. However, one child's cluster of signs may be quite different from another's. Furthermore, all the various symptoms of dyslexia may be interpreted in relation to the traits in Chapters Two, Three and Four – and be associated with anxiety or tension.

Can dyslexia be explained more satisfactorily by reference to the child's personality? My answer to this question is a definite "Yes". Children with dyslexia appear to experience switch-offs or to have a certain degree of tension or anxiety which can usually be seen to have existed prior to the literacy problems. This level of anxiety may well be within normal limits so that the youngsters might not appear particularly anxious.

There may be just a few current minor signs, such as continued daytime thumb-sucking in a ten-year-old, a "deepness", a refusal to do something at all if it cannot be done very well – the possibilities seem endless. If we dismiss these clues, and those from the past, simply because the behaviour is not abnormal, or if we lay them solely at the door of the dyslexic difficulties (saying the children are anxious because they are dyslexic), then we might well fail to recognise what the problem may be – *that the child has become programmed to be unable to engage his brain properly.* Genetic links for dyslexia may indeed be associated with anxiety and responses to it.

The stigma surrounding the word anxiety prevents many of us from appreciating that it is not only a normal component of us all but essential to our lives if we are to be useful. Much of our reasonable, instinctive behaviour results from normal anxiety – but reasonable behaviour can cause problems. It is perfectly understandable that a normal, sensitive and perhaps generally confident four or five-year-old might feel uneasy or try too hard when being encouraged to learn to read and write and find himself experiencing a protective shutdown device which is perhaps already quite well established in him.

The situation is understandably complicated by the stress which dyslexia itself creates.

BRAIN STRUCTURES

Many researchers are now using the latest brain-imaging technology to identify differences in brain structure or brain activity between people with specific disabilities (or abilities) and those without them. It is, of course, necessary to consider cause and effect in these matters. Rather than be the cause of problems, the differences which are found may be an effect of an underlying causal factor – they may be a manifestation of a problem.

Nevertheless, such studies are bringing interesting information to light. Professor Uta Frith and colleagues (Paulesu et al., 1996) have shown, through the administration of positron emission tomography, that in contrast to normal controls, certain areas of the brain of subjects suffering from dyslexia were not activated in concert during phonological processing. The researchers found that the major sites of the phonological system could be activated by their dyslexic subjects separately, but not together. They suggest that dyslexia is a problem of disconnection.

It is sensible to consider here that Donna Williams views her more global difficulties which feature in her autism as a problem of poor connection. In this way she explains her frequent inability to process for meaning and significance and her delayed or unsatisfactory responses (Williams, 1996).

Problems with connection may be common to both dyslexia and autism and my observations and enquiries lead me to believe that a degree of early shutdown is likely to be a contributory or causal factor in each case. The nature of the resulting problems would depend upon the nature of the shutdown – how selective or global it has been programmed to be, and whether one has reacted negatively to emotional involvement, as in the case of autism.

THE SYMPTOMS

Dyslexia is just one group of symptoms which can be related to anxiety and which people find helpful to isolate. But many children have a few of the symptoms, such as a real difficulty in planning and writing essays, using a dictionary or remembering arrangements which revolve around dates, without any general reading or writing problems. These people are unlikely to be diagnosed as dyslexic yet they have difficulties which distress them and which are not properly recognised by others nor understood by themselves.

Let us take a look at the signs of dyslexia, as listed in the British Dyslexia Association's booklet, *Dyslexia in Primary Schools*. The Association points out that, "Not every sign or symptom of the dyslexic profile presents itself in each dyslexic person, although there is usually evident a sufficient cluster of these signs to lead to a diagnosis." Having followed the previous chapters of this book, the reader will be able to appreciate that these signs could be related to switching off and tension or anxiety (note in particular the symptoms which suggest switching off in the early preschool or pre-reading years). It may indeed be the case that such learning difficulties often run in families (Stevenson et al., 1987) because personality-related factors are inherited.

Before School

- History of slow speech development.
- Difficulty learning nursery rhymes.
- Finds phonological difficulty with the selection of the odd one out, e.g., cat; mat; pig; fat.
- Slow in name finding.
- Some dyslexic children enjoy being read to, but show no interest in letters or words. Others have no patience for sitting and listening.
- Often accused of not listening or 'not paying attention'.
- Poor understanding of prepositions.
- Difficulty with two or more instructions at one time, but well able to carry out tasks when presented in smaller units.
- Difficulty keeping simple rhythm.
- May not crawl – but walks early.
- Persistent difficulty in dressing.
- Difficulty with shoe laces, buttons, clothes the right way round.
- Difficulty with catching, kicking or throwing a ball.
- Difficulty with hopping and/or skipping.
- Excessive tripping, bumping into things and falling over things.
- Obvious 'good' and 'bad' days, for no apparent reason.

At Primary School

- Personal organisation poor.
- Poor time keeping and awareness.
- Difficulty in remembering what day of the week it is, his birth date, seasons of the year, months of the year.
- Difficulty in learning to tell the time.
- Difficulty remembering anything in a sequential order, e.g., days of the week, the alphabet, tables, foreign languages.
- Poor reading progress – particularly on look-and-say methods.
- Inability to blend letters together.
- Difficulty in establishing syllable division, beginnings and endings of words, synthesis and analysis of words.
- Hesitant and laboured reading especially when reading aloud, often misses out words or adds extra words or fails to recognise familiar words.
- Making anagrams of words, e.g., tired for tried, breaded for bearded.
- Undetermined hand preference.
- Confusion between left and right.
- Poor handwriting with many reversals and badly formed letters.
- Difficulty in picking out the most important points from a passage.
- Poor standards of written work in comparison with oral ability.
- Losing the point of the story being written or read.
- Messy work with many crossings out and words tried several times, e.g., wippe, wype, wiep, wipe.
- Persistent confusion with letters which look similar, particularly b/d, p/g, p/q, n/u, m/w.
- Confusion with number order, e.g., units, tens, hundreds.
- Confusion with symbols, e.g., + and x signs.
- A word spelt several different ways in one piece of writing.
- Badly set out written work; inability to stay close to the margin.
- Seems to 'dream' – does not seem to listen.
- Easily distracted.
- Limited understanding of non-verbal communication.

- Fine motor skills might be poor, leading to weaknesses in the speed, control and accuracy of the pencil.

- May become the class clown, disruptive or withdrawn.

- Employs work avoidance tactics (sharpening pencils, looking for books, etc.).

- Rests head on desk or right over to one side when colouring or writing.

- Performs unevenly day to day.

- Excessive tiredness.

It might happen that a child complains about words moving or becoming blurred when he tries to read or learn to spell; sometimes the words seem to form a black mass. It is known that blurring can be stress-related (a visual disturbance occurring as an aftereffect of visual sharpening in stress). One youth known to me could only read one page at a go; when he forced himself to turn the page and continue reading, he experienced a sudden convulsive seizure, never having had one before.

Anxiety or conditioned patterns of behaviour may cause the brain not to be properly engaged for a task. There might be switching off, slowness of thought and difficulty processing for meaning or connecting ideas, with panic reactions and possibly some avoidance strategies. This can lead to problems in assimilating and retrieving information and so to an apparent inability to develop literacy skills, to name just one of the possible learning difficulties which may result.

With an understanding, we are in a better position to devise a remedy for these reading and writing difficulties. We can appreciate why the child might be failing. We can see that since he is programmed to fail when he follows whatever is his usual practice, we have to change our tactics. We need to help him develop some alternative behaviour of the brain.

I have devised the following method to help young children who are at risk of developing dyslexia or experiencing reading, writing and spelling difficulties (but do not have severe problems of demand avoidance or compulsive negativity – or any other problem which interferes with the development of motivation to learn). We know that the child probably fears failure and expects his usual responses to occur – *so we eliminate the possibility of failing.*

Let us suppose that he still cannot really read at all, although he might be able to sound some letters. Perhaps he memorises the sentences in a pretence of reading. He is given a beginner's book belonging to a reading scheme – and the more simple the book, the better it is for some children. A reading scheme which amuses parents but has rather sophisticated humour is not helpful to a child who may have problems understanding the books, for instance; we do not want to encourage a divorce of the mechanics of reading from meaning. Another thing to be borne in mind is a child's tendency to call any task boring which he finds threatening – a 'boring' book may be at least of potential interest to him. Once a suitable scheme has been selected, the no failure method may be implemented.

METHOD BASED ON NO FAILURE

Any method of assisting the process of reading, writing and spelling must necessarily be adapted to suit the child's particular needs; the degree of repetition required and the speed at which one progresses are thus highly variable. As a general principle the adult should be in touch with the child's feelings, so that he knows exactly what the youngster is capable of doing at a particular time. With this no failure method the child is not actually asked to read the words, and on realising this he is generally able to relax. Indeed, the adult might begin by saying that there is no need for the child to read the book – that the intention is to play some little games with it.

Having chosen an appropriate book, which will have only one, or perhaps two short sentences per page, the adult might read the entire book to the child. If the well-weathered *One, Two, Three and Away!* scheme (written by Sheila McCullagh and published by Collins Educational) were being used, for example, the adult would then return to the first page and say, "Here is Roger Red-hat", pointing in turn to each word as it is spoken (Introductory Book A). Then he says, "Which word do you want me to point to? You choose a word for me to point to", rereading the words as much as seems necessary to help the child and allowing him to help hold the book. When a word has been selected and duly pointed to, the adult chooses one from the remaining words for the child to point to, repeating and drawing attention to the text again, in a relaxed way and as much as is necessary to ensure success. Such a procedure could be repeated for say, two or even three more pages, so that the adult and child have perhaps covered, 'Here is Roger Red-hat', 'Here is Roger's hat', 'Roger's hat is red', 'Rip is Roger's dog' and 'Here is Mr. Red-hat'. The youngster is being encouraged to scan for words (this being an important skill for the future). He is likely to be giving the sentences more than a cursory glance and, hopefully, he is enjoying himself. Although he does not know a word well enough to be able to read it on a flash card, he may have enough recognition of it (or of its adjoining words) to be able to select it without a lot of repetition and he will know he has achieved something – or at least that he has not failed.

In order to reinforce positive feelings, the first page might be returned to and the adult says, "See this word, 'Here'. Let's see how many times we can find it in the book." Turning to page two, he asks, "Is it anywhere on this page?" and so on throughout the book. The child will find that the word occurs four times, and during the process he is likely to be happily involved in the activity, engaging his brain and paying at least some attention to detail. The frequency of occurrence of the word 'red' might be discovered next.

At this point, one boosts the child's confidence by showing him that he can write words from memory. We must allow him to attend to and absorb the word without anxiety, in the same way as other children do. In order to achieve this, the adult selects an appropriate word from the youngster's reading book – and it may well be necessary or sensible to begin with two letter words. The word is written on a piece of paper and given to the child to absorb. He is told to take as long as he likes to get to know it and to tell the adult when he is ready for it to be removed; he must then write it out with a pencil. But he is warned that he has to write it out in its entirety. If he begins to make a mistake, his efforts will be completely erased or his paper folded over to remove his attempt, and he will have to view the word again. The adult observes his technique of learning. Should his lips start to move in a desperate, mechanical effort to sound out each letter of the word individually, he is stopped. He is told that he is trying too hard. He is told to stop trying and just look at the word, and he is reminded in a cheerful way to take as long as he likes. He must sense a spirit of fun in the activity, that it is rather like a game with a bit of a challenge, as he aims to write the word correctly after one viewing.

Next, each word of a sentence which has been utilised in the book can be written on its own separate piece of paper, the child contributing to the activity as far as he is able (using the method just described). He may then be gently encouraged to participate in arranging the words to form the sentence and perhaps even a second one. After drawing a picture of Roger Red-hat he might, for example, help in rearranging below it, 'Here is Roger Red-hat' to make it read, 'Roger Red-hat is here.' Similarly, 'Roger's hat is red' may become 'is Roger's hat red?' He might like to draw Rip and help organise the words 'Here is Rip' or 'Here is Roger's dog' underneath his picture.

When the child has become familiar with the words, they can be written on individual pieces of paper and hidden around the room, a few at a time. (Allow him to choose which to hide.) His task is to find each one and say what he has found, if able. If he does not instantly know the word, he is told it immediately; for example, "Good, you've found *has*." Take turns with the child to hide and find.

Little pieces of paper may be preferable to smart cards or formal looking flashcards which might seem forbidding to the child if they are associated with past failure. The pieces of paper are acceptable to him because nobody is asking him to name the words on them. After the session they should be thrown away. If they are needed again, they can be rewritten; this avoids any staleness or fear of not remembering exactly what was remembered before, and it gives further practice.

It is important that one does not tax the child's abilities. He is more likely to respond to a challenge if it is not too large and proves enjoyable. We must stop him as soon as he starts to make an error when writing a word or letter (and renew the process of absorption) for it is necessary to avoid negative feelings and feedback as far as possible. Generally it is not long before the child is delighted to find that he can write a phrase or sentence made from two or three of the words. Should he make an error, however, he must still return to the beginning, which in this instance is the beginning of the first word. He is thus encouraged to reabsorb the entire sentence and receives extra practice at something which he finds relatively effortless.

In this way the book can be held on to by the child for at least a week or two, with plenty of activity and no sense of boredom or failure associated with it. He does not fail because *he is not encouraged to read a word* unless it becomes apparent that he not only knows it well, but is able to recall or retrieve it well. When he moves on to the next book in the scheme he finds that he already knows or partially knows some of the words in it and they now seem friendly to him rather than threatening.

A youngster may well benefit from repeating the word absorption exercise with particular words for revision purposes. The learning is more easily committed to memory, since he is actively and enthusiastically involved in the process rather than copying words in a switched off mode. Once confidence is gained and some negative behaviour ousted, he is often able to spell the word many weeks later.

The adult should be cautious about offering suggestions which are intended to be helpful. He or she might even need to desist from suggesting ways of breaking down the word into parts or saying that it is one of those *sk* words, etc. We have to bear in mind that the child is likely to have negative feelings regarding instructions, so that it may be expedient to avoid them as far as is possible during this early stage, and we certainly do not want to say things he has heard before. We must be relaxed and give him the opportunity to relax and enjoy the task. Moreover, a young child with dyslexic difficulties and no confidence in his learning ability is unlikely to be able to absorb, retain and retrieve spelling rules and lists of words with similar spellings.

But he forgets...

The reader may well be thinking, "What about the child who can read one moment but has forgotten it all the next?" If negative feelings and pro-gramming are strong and the child is low in confidence and self-esteem with regard to literacy skills, retrieval may be poor. As long as we reinforce his learning in a cheerful, relaxed way, and *do not put his recall to the test*, he will not be receiving negative recall experiences. His confidence will grow as his positive feelings and experiences replace the negative ones and he no longer practises failing nor expects to fail. He will not be receiving the impression that people think it is time he knew certain words and he will not feel that his progress is being monitored or assessed. This situation is, of course, harder to bring about if the pressure is all or mainly coming from within the child himself, but a little real progress will be followed by more – once the youngster can properly and regularly engage his mind, he can succeed.

Difficulty forming letters

If the child seems unable to form letters, the following method may well prove helpful:

1. Help him to grasp the pencil correctly.

2. Guide his hand to form a suitable letter.

3. After he has formed the letter several times with your guidance, gradu-ally remove some of the pressure of your hand on his, so that he learns to make, let us say, the last part of the movement for the letter. Do not ex-pect him to form the entire letter on his own in one go – it can be a joint effort while he gradually assumes more responsibility for its creation.

Writing Sentences

Once a child becomes confident in his absorption of spellings he might like to try writing an entire sentence which contains only words with which he is competent. (He might enjoy helping to compose the sentence, too.) If he is happy and relaxed about this, he may begin to prevent or counteract a spell-ing problem through positive experiences. Since an error results in an immediate reviewing of the sentence and a fresh start, beginning with the first word again, the amount of practice carried out is appropriate to and determined by the youngster's performance.

Sometimes an older child has patchy spelling ability, being able to spell some difficult or less common words yet having problems with many more simple ones or those which recur frequently. One might give him a simple sentence to write, noting any incorrectly spelt words for the specific practice later. Mastering the more frequently occurring and the more simple words will naturally be confidence building.

Rushing

It is often the case that a rather tense child rushes when reading (and probably when speaking), passing over words without paying any attention to detail. Even though he may have a reasonable reading age, he may have spelling difficulties which result from this inattention to detail. Absorbing single words and combining them in sentences in the manner I have described gives exactly the practice required by these children. Enjoying the challenge and being totally involved in the activity enables the youngster to pay attention to detail in a way he is not accustomed to do; returning to the beginning of the sentence every time an error is made leads to an increase in motivation and practice. (If the child has spelling lists to learn for school the words can be combined in sentences in this manner and learned in a spirit of fun.) An eight-year-old with a below average reading age and poor spelling ability will typically have soon correctly written a sentence such as "It was night but he could see the creature beneath the tree", having some minutes earlier had difficulty spelling *night, could, creature* and *beneath*. Since the words have been learned in a happy, relaxed mood, they are better remembered.

Whatever we choose to do with the child, we must ensure that he is not encouraged to practise writing in a state of unease or panic, with poor concentration or with a brain which is not adequately engaged for the activity. Since sentences are more likely to become disordered through negative programming and switch-off or shutdown rather than through inherent inability, it would not be in a child's interest if we were to draw attention to all his written errors, including grammatical ones. He cannot learn in an anxious state or with a brain which has not been properly engaged for the task, so he cannot profit in the least by having his failings brought to his attention. The mistakes (word omissions and poor word order or usage, for example) reduce and increase according to his state of mind.

If an older child bunches up his words so that they seem to run into each other, it may be that he is writing mechanically rather than properly engaging his brain. If a youngster keeps breaking pencil leads, this may be a sign that he is tense. We must note all possible signs of his tension.

BREAKING DOWN TASKS

In its 'Before School' list of symptoms of dyslexia the British Dyslexia Association includes *"Difficulty with two or more instructions at one time, but well able to carry out tasks when presented in smaller units."* The child can seem overwhelmed by the sheer quantity or enormity of a task. (There is often, for example, a noticeable improvement in spelling when single sentences are attempted, rather than large chunks of work.) This problem may follow the youngster through his school days so that homework can be a great worry to him and when aged sixteen and faced with an examination paper, there may be a kind of mental collapse. The teenager might be expected to perform well in the paper, if he has a good grasp of his subject, and his teacher is puzzled by his low examination scores.

Fortunately, our modern examinations are helpful in their design, since the number of marks allocated to each question is shown beside the question. This gives us the means of deciding how much time should be spent on say, two or three short questions, and enables the student to have a short-term goal. When one sits down with the troubled person and breaks the questions down into smaller units, the improvement can be staggering. It is particularly helpful to set a timer going, saying for example, "See if you can answer these three questions in the seven minutes you are allowed". The youngster may well find that he has time left over and his confidence grows as he discovers that he is equal to the smaller challenges. He should then be encouraged to go off to analyse and familiarise himself with other similar examination papers. It is satisfying to see him lose his fear and start to enjoy doing the papers.

We have rather jumped in time from the early school years to school leaving age. There will, of course, be countless opportunities in between for helping the child by breaking down tasks into less daunting, smaller units. Some children with dyslexic problems are painfully slow when they are reading and writing. This method of breaking down tasks and timing them is an excellent means of gaining speed, for the child is actively involved – but of course it must only be used with tasks which he is capable of doing.

The organisation and writing of essays can be facilitated by the method. Although the youngster may initially need help or encouragement in formulating a brief paragraph plan, he is likely to engage his mind better if he is then given a limited amount of time to write his first very short paragraph – and the timer may be set in front of him, as his challenge. Each paragraph can be treated separately in this manner. A positive response is always given to the work achieved, no matter what the standard. As involvement and confidence grow, so may the ability to construct the essay plan itself.

***

It will be appreciated that the earlier problems arising from dyslexia are dealt with, the better, not simply because the child has not lost so much ground, but because he will not be so strongly programmed to fail. If one observes the youngster well, the difficulties might be prevented. Whenever a method or approach is not working, it should be altered, but another point which is important for us to bear in mind and which I have tried to highlight, is that when dealing with a child with dyslexic-type difficulties it is not enough to know what to do with him. We must also know what *not* to do with him.

No matter what a person's age, when literacy problems are dealt with there is an increase in confidence and frequently a simultaneous improvement in speech and language, if there has previously been a difficulty. This is because the underlying factors in speech and language difficulties are often the same as those underlying literacy problems (anxiety and programmed difficulties with connection, absorption, retention and retrieval). When we address the one, we are addressing the other. Literacy problems tend to be viewed by the sufferer as his greatest stumbling block, so that their remediation is likely to produce the greatest reduction in anxiety. Since anxiety and its effects on programming can be a major factor in confused, disjointed, inaccurate or inarticulate speech, and in inattention to one's own speech or to that of others (see Chapter Four), there is likely to be a spin-off of improved verbal comprehension and expressive language.

Finally, when one is involved with children with dyslexia, it is important to be alert to the symptoms of depression (see Chapter Nine). Sluggish thinking and poor absorption and recall of information, coupled with excessive tiredness and performance variability are particularly noteworthy symptoms which can be shared by the two conditions.

SUMMARY OF THE NO FAILURE METHOD

1. If a young child is experiencing literacy difficulties, utilise a very basic reading scheme which has a lot of carry-over of words from one book to the next, and a lot of repetition thereafter.

2. Read the book to the child, pointing to the words. Help him to become a little familiar with and take some notice of individual words by encouraging him to point to a word that you have just pointed to while you were reading a sentence to him. Point to all the words as much as seems necessary to help him, and encourage him to ask you to point to a word he chooses, too. Let the child count how many times a particular word occurs in the book.

3. Write the first word of one of the short (perhaps three word) sentences, and tell him what it says. Then ask him to look at it for as long as he wishes and tell you when he is ready to write it himself. When he thinks he is ready to have a go at writing it, remove the word, giving him a blank piece of paper and pencil. (Paper can be exchanged for keyboards and computers for children with a physical impairment.)

4. *As soon as* the child begins to make a mistake or hesitate for more than a second, show him the word (and name it for him) again so that he can repeat the exercise in absorption. Repeat this as often as necessary, keeping quiet and relaxed yourself. Avoid any pressure or lavish praise. Try not to give any message that you are eager for him to succeed quickly, and avoid additional instructions. Try to make it seem like a game or little challenge, but do not imply that it is easy. NEVER ALLOW THE CHILD TO STRUGGLE when writing a word; observe him carefully and always be ready to jump in and show him the word again as soon as he needs help. Do not allow him to correct a mistake; always remove his effort and start the absorption process again. When he decides he's ready for it, present him with blank paper again – his mistake can be folded over.

5. Once the child has written the word successfully, move on to the next word in the sentence. When he is successful with this one too, name and let him view the two words of the sentence together and write them both when he feels ready. Should he make a mistake on the second word, he views both words again and begins once again to write both words, beginning with the first. (This gives extra, relaxed practice with the first word and reinforces it.)

6. When he has written both words together correctly, introduce the third word of the sentence, following the same procedure. When he has

written it correctly, read all three words and give them to him to view together. Remember that *as soon as* the child makes a mistake he must view the entire sentence again and begin it again on more blank paper.

7. NEVER TEST THE CHILD to see if he has remembered the words. The aim is to change habits by allowing him to relax, absorb words and their sounds, and maintain concentration. He will not be able to remember and retrieve words instantly. His confidence and belief in his own ability has to be gradually built up.

8. Practice can be varied by mixing words from different sentences or encouraging the child to rearrange words written individually on separate pieces of paper (for example, *here is Ben* can become *Ben is here)*. A picture of Ben might be drawn and labelled.

9. When the child has become really familiar with the words, they can be written on individual pieces of paper and hidden around the room, a few at a time. (Allow him to choose which to hide.) His task is to find each one and say what he has found, if able. If he does not instantly know the word, he is told it immediately; for example, "Good, you've found *has.*" (He may feel more relaxed, and hence be more successful, if he plays this game with an older sibling who can read.) Take turns with the child to hide and find.

10. Once the child's confidence and ability to absorb, retain and retrieve information has grown, some words might be casually sounded during the practice. The adult should, however, be wary of offering any detailed instruction concerning letters and their sound combinations too early.

With this method we eliminate the possibility of failure. The child is not encouraged to read a word unless it becomes apparent that he can recall or retrieve it with ease. He dictates his own pace and he does not experience the harmful negative feelings brought about when his progress is tested or monitored. He can therefore relax and absorb the information, and new learning pathways are opened up.

Older children with literacy difficulties

The method can be adapted for older children (and adults). A variety of appropriate sentences can be given, utilising this no struggle and no failure approach. The same words might be placed in different sentences for their reinforcement. Words from school spelling lists can be included in suitable sentences for older children to absorb and practise. Should the person forget the sentence itself as he is writing, it should be repeated for him in its entirety, not word by word as he writes.

CHAPTER SEVEN

HYPERACTIVITY/ATTENTION DEFICIT HYPERACTIVITY DISORDER (A.D.H.D.) AND EXCESS TENSION

I have used the term *Attention Deficit Hyperactivity Disorder* rather than *Attention Deficit Disorder* in order to distinguish those children who have a problem attending and are mentally and often physically hyperactive from those who are inattentive (because of, for example, switching off and avoidance) but not generally hyperactive. It is important to note that, although a child may not seem particularly physically hyperactive, he may be so mentally. The labels 'hyperactive' and 'Attention Deficit Hyperactivity Disorder' are useful in drawing people's attention to the difficulties met by the youngsters and their families but, as will become apparent, the symptoms cannot be neatly isolated from all the other personality traits exhibited by children.

Listed below are some symptoms of hyperactivity which have been collated by the Hyperactive Children's Support Group. The group points out that there are degrees of the problem and that not every child will have all the symptoms. The reader will be able to see that, once again, they are all symptoms which can be related to tension or anxiety. The word 'tense' often seems more fitting than 'anxious', however, when one describes the child. He generally seems to be in a state of tension which makes him more than usually keyed up to do things or have things done; he might be irritable or excited.

In Infancy

- Crying, screaming, restlessness; some need little sleep.
- Colic; very difficult to feed, whether breast or bottle.
- Cannot be pacified or cuddled; spurn affection.
- Excessive dribbling; may be very thirsty.
- Headbanging, cot rocking, fits and tantrums.

In Older Children *(in addition to symptoms in infancy)*

- Clumsy, impulsive; often accident prone.
- Erratic, disruptive behaviour.
- Compulsive 'touching'; constant motion.
- Disturb other children; may be aggressive.
- Lack concentration and may be withdrawn.
- Normal or high IQ but fail at school.
- Poor appetite; poor hand and eye co-ordination.
- Unco-operative behaviour.
- Self-abusive (pulling hair, picking skin, etc.).
- Continued problems with sleep.

The Support Group also refers to obsessions, social problems, speech and language difficulties, fidgeting, distractibility, ability to create havoc, high pain thresholds and hypersensitivity leading to allergies (for example, food allergies). Other observers refer to disorganisation, boredom, excitability, insatiability, egocentricity, low self-esteem and depression.

Let us look at some examples.

Nicholas

Nicholas's mother had received oxytocin to accelerate a long labour and the analgesic, pethidine. He was jaundiced and very sleepy during his first few days but he erupted into a temper upon awakening and during feeds.

Although Nicholas walked on his first birthday, he was always falling over – to the extent that he was seen by an orthopaedic surgeon (who was unable to find anything wrong with him). During the next few years he paid many visits to the casualty department of the local hospital. He loved to rush about, climb and swing but fell from climbing frames, ponies and trees. His enthusiasm knew no bounds and seemed to deprive him of thoughts of safety. He rushed at things and his timing was ill-judged. He was poor at throwing and catching a ball. He was heavy footed when he walked, and needed to be reminded how to hold a pencil to good effect.

Nicholas had a tendency to splutter out his words and his vocal resonance was poor. He had been late to stop dribbling and he paid so little attention to what he was doing that he made numerous mistakes when copying out things at school. His teacher complained that he was always first out of the classroom when the bell rang – he would even break off in the middle of a word. He could, however, show a lot of enthusiasm in the classroom when something interested him, when he might absorb concepts and information effortlessly. Teachers welcomed his enthusiasm at times, but resented it when it led to the spilling of paints, etc.

Nicholas's clumsiness was uneven. He started to play the electric guitar and his teacher found him to be an incredibly fast learner. It was noticeable, however, that his performance varied according to his motivation for sometimes he kept in time and on other occasions he did not. He became good at skate-boarding and table-tennis. In short, he became good at anything he really wanted to do, as long as it did not require prolonged concentration and organisation on his part; activities needed to be of a fluid nature or broken down into stages for him.

Although Nicholas did not resist cuddles he never sought them. His mother said that he was a fidget to hold and he continued in this restless manner, never appearing to sit without fidgeting, or fiddling with some item. He had always to be restrained from touching ornaments in people's houses or items in shops. Indeed, he fiddled with anything within reach. Being unable to sustain his interest in a toy or to play imaginatively, he soon grew bored and was hard to keep occupied.

Mealtimes were important to Nicholas for he seemed to love all food and had a very large appetite. At the end of one meal he would ask what he would be getting for the next one. Similarly, during a school outing to London he had quizzed his headteacher about the day's agenda; they might all be in the middle of watching the changing of the guards, but what were they going to do next?

New clothes, new school bags and equipment or a new bicycle delighted Nicholas as they do other children, but no matter how good his initial intentions were, in no time at all they were damaged or in a mess. He was blissfully unaware that he was dragging his open school bag through oily puddles and it was rare for there to be two football boots in his games bag. He was the first to get changed after a games period at school but might well have his shirt incorrectly buttoned or his jumper on inside out and at least one item of clothing would usually be left behind on the floor. His mother complained that his bedroom was always in a state of disorder; items were just abandoned, never put away, and there was not a pen in sight that was not cracked and leaking because it had been chewed. He was distractible, impatient, always in a hurry, and often his attention was elsewhere.

Although Nicholas had a low level of tolerance or a 'short fuse' he was obedient and although he was apt to fall into a temper easily he never threw things or became aggressive in any way, either to others or towards himself. His tears seemed to result from impatience, frustration and general misery; he did not blame others or harbour grudges. Discipline was never a problem at home or at school, where Nicholas always met with consistency, yet there were difficulties at school, particularly of a social nature.

Initially he had joined in some of the playground games but a teacher explained to his mother that he was inattentive to the rules and the games soon bored him; he was not a co-operative playmate. Being somewhat egocentric he began to act silly amid all the excitement, looking for ways to change the activity. He showed little sign of inhibition among others and soon became a target for bullying. But it was never his intention to cause problems and he was often deeply distressed and panicky when his behaviour got him into any trouble.

Nicholas was not markedly obsessional or fond of routine although he did like a routine and he had a temporary slight preoccupation with trains. He was an ardent and persistent thumb-sucker.

Nicholas was a bright boy who was encumbered by hyperactivity and a difficulty in attending. He was not simply an intelligent person who grew restless and irritable because there were not enough interesting and challenging activities for him. He was an intelligent child who could not involve himself in such activities, unless they excited him or were broken down into short steps, for otherwise his concentration could not be sustained. He had difficulty, therefore, in carrying out tasks which entailed a lot of organisation. These problems affected his school work, his personal relationships and, eventually, his general confidence.

Jeremy

Jeremy was slow to speak. He was a hyperactive three-year-old who mumbled and indulged in some repetitive questioning. He had a tendency to ignore people, when he would look quite vacant; at other times he would appear alert, with darting eyes. He regularly overreacted to events, sometimes becoming aggressive towards people and he pinched himself. He ate large quantities of food, but restricted the variety. He restlessly fiddled with things but would not play with anything for long. His mother doubted that a toy shop could occupy him for any reasonable length of time.

Jeremy was independent at playgroup. He would never sit still to do anything, preferring to climb or to ride a bicycle. During his early years his mother could not leave him in his pushchair for a single minute while she collected shopping bags together, without precipitating a rage. Shopping trips tended to be stressful. Soon after reaching the shops, Jeremy would begin to cry because he had been made to sit still for some time; later, when he had outgrown his pushchair, he complained noisily about walking. Awakening after a mid-day nap was a distressing and rage-provoking experience for him and keeping him happy while his parents ate their meals was often a test of their ingenuity. The little boy's mother tried to teach him to play imaginatively but he viewed her efforts as a form of entertainment. He did not attend to the television, except briefly for a cartoon.

Jeremy's answer to boredom was to yell in protest or to lie on the floor sucking his thumb. His mother said that the carpet in his room was littered with little bits of wool pulled from his blanket and stuffed into his nostril with a circular movement of his index finger, while he sucked his thumb. He had no interest in any soft toy.

Liam

Teachers at Liam's comprehensive school warned that he should keep a low profile and stop making himself so obvious. One predicted that he would get his nose broken some day – and he did. If an entire class was misbehaving, he was the youngster most stimulated, and hence most noticed.

Liam was a seventeen-year-old boy who stammered. He had lost most of his former more obvious signs of hyperactivity but learning difficulties remained. Although he found revising for G.C.S.E. examinations quite impossible, he fared well in the examination part of the assessments; he particularly favoured multi-choice questions. When his teacher marked a practice G.C.S.E. mathematics paper she had given him, she was amazed to find that much of the working had been omitted. Liam had found the correct answers quickly, and on discussing the paper with him, the teacher discovered that he had cut one or two 'unnecessary' corners in thinking. G.C.S.E. coursework held no advantages for him. It required concentration and organisation which he was unable to muster. He struggled to keep his head above water academically, doing the bare minimum and giving unfinished work in late.

Although Liam found academic work difficult to begin and organise, he was a reliable and conscientious employee, keeping the same holiday job each year, and always showing initiative. As long as there were plenty of things going on, he was happy.

***

Most hyperactive, inattentive children gradually lose their more obvious symptoms as they mature and their uninhibited behaviour becomes controlled. They may well employ strategies to cope with their excess tension – they perhaps seem laid-back and may appear to have opted out of things. They may still be likely to walk through dirt rather than step over it, to leave gates open, and to forget the towel when they go swimming but so too may they be capable of inspired thinking when their enthusiasm is sparked.

Some people who were hyperactive as children go through life experiencing difficulties with relationships, overreacting, being distractible and finding it hard to concentrate and organise themselves. They may become alcoholics, suffer from depression or have problems such as obsessive-compulsive behaviour. Fortunately most hyperactive children greatly improve with maturity and fare well; many are highly successful people.

The reader will appreciate, from the wide range of symptoms which can be associated with hyperactivity (i.e. symptoms associated with tension or anxiety), that any number of combinations are possible. Since hyperactivity may be combined with a diversity of other traits, there can be no highly typical hyperactive child.

TESTING

In their book, *Attention Deficit Disorder*, Edward Hallowell and John Ratey explain that testing procedures can temporarily treat A.D.H.D. and mask the symptoms. The novelty, the one-to-one attention and the highly structured situation where tasks are short and well-contained all help to stimulate, focus and sustain interest. Well above average test results may then reinforce a general impression that a child "can do it" and suspicions that he is wilful or lazy may seem confirmed.

CHAPTER EIGHT

AUTISM IN THE LIGHT OF PERSONALITY TRAITS

In 1943 Dr. Leo Kanner, emeritus Professor of Child Psychiatry at Johns Hopkins University, Baltimore, became the first person to publish an account of autism. In 1961 a British working party under the chairmanship of Dr. Mildred Creek produced a report which tentatively offered nine points to help in the diagnosis of the condition. These were:

1. Gross and sustained impairment of emotional relationships with people. This includes the more usual aloofness and the empty clinging (so-called symbiosis); also abnormal behaviour towards other people as persons, such as using them, or parts of them, impersonally. Difficulty in mixing and playing with other children is often outstanding and long-lasting.

2. Apparent unawareness of his own personal identity to a degree inappropriate to his age. This may be seen in abnormal behaviour towards himself, such as posturing or exploration and scrutiny of parts of his body. Repeated self-directed aggression, sometimes resulting in actual damage, may be another aspect of his lack of integration (see also point 5), as may be the confusion of personal pronouns (see point 7).

3. Pathological preoccupation with particular objects or certain characteristics of them, without regard to their accepted functions.

4. Sustained resistance to change in the environment and a striving to maintain or restore sameness. In some instances behaviour appears to aim at producing a state of perceptual monotony.

5. Abnormal perceptual experience (in the absence of discernible organic abnormality) is implied by excessive, diminished or unpredictable response to sensory stimuli – for example, visual and auditory avoidance, insensitivity to pain and temperature.

6. Acute, excessive and seemingly illogical anxiety is a frequent phenomenon. This tends to be precipitated by change, whether in material environment or in routine, as well as by temporary interruption of a

symbiotic attachment to persons or things. (Apparently commonplace phenomena or objects seem to become invested with terrifying qualities. On the other hand, an appropriate sense of fear in the face of real danger may be lacking.)

7. Speech may have been lost or never acquired, or may have failed to develop beyond a level appropriate to an earlier stage. There may be confusion of personal pronouns, echolalia, or other mannerisms of use and diction. Though words or phrases may be uttered, they may convey no sense of ordinary communication.

8. Distortion in mobility patterns; for example, (a) excess as in hyperkinesis, (b) immobility as in catatonia, (c) bizarre postures, or ritualistic mannerisms, such as rocking and spinning (themselves or objects).

9. A background of serious retardation in which islets of normal, near-normal or exceptional intellectual function or skill may appear.

Kanner and Creek were describing the more severe manifestations of autism and not the milder degrees which are now acknowledged to be common. I refer to Creek's working party's nine points because, unlike some other definitions of autism, they do draw attention to the acute anxiety frequently suffered by these children (point 6).

The reader will be able to recognise that the above nine points feature within the personality traits described in Chapters Two, Three and Four of this book. The difference between youngsters with autism and other children is in the degree of their symptoms and the extent to which they interfere with normal social relationships and communication.

In 1944 Hans Asperger, a child psychologist working in Vienna, published a paper called *Autistic Psychopathies in Childhood*. He was interested in intelligent, able children with difficulties of an autistic nature. He described verbal but socially naive and clumsy children who use language for their own specific interests rather than for social communication.

Over the years it has become recognised by many of those working closely with young children that autism is a spectrum of difficulties of varying severity – that there is a continuum; one child might have the mildest of symptoms, whereas another might have very severe ones, and there is a multitude of conditions in between. In the mid 1970s I began to view autism in terms of a continuum after seeing various degrees of autistic-like traits in many normal children in my clinics. However, in the 1980s it also became clear to me that I was merely seeing *particular combinations of personality traits*. If literacy skills were most affected, *dyslexia* was the word used to describe the problems; if excess activity and inattention were the more obvious or more serious symptoms, then the behaviour was called *hyperactive*; if language difficulties were prominent there might be a *receptive language* disorder or a *semantic-pragmatic* problem (a difficulty comprehending, recalling and using words and in processing and using language practically); if tics were the most obvious manifestation of tension and compulsion, then *Tourette syndrome* might be named, and if human relationships were sufficiently impaired by withdrawn, obsessive and compulsive behaviour, the term *autism* might be applied, albeit usually tentatively. But the traits show themselves throughout all the various conditions, overlapping here and there without any clear order and they appear to share the common factor, anxiety – sometimes in the form of fear or tension.

It can be argued that children with autism are highly anxious because they have so many problems. This is likely to be true, but perhaps unlikely to be the whole story. When the statement is turned around and we consider the possibility that the children have so many problems because of initial, or early, anxiety or tension related responses (i.e. various degrees of withdrawal or shutdown), autism is easier to comprehend.

It is noteworthy that people who are more obviously affected by autism rarely become really normal. If anxiety can cause symptoms, why can't it be lost, removed or considerably lessened and the autism disappear? It is necessary to consider that the child may not have well-established normal thought and behaviour patterns to fall into (unlike the person who suffers from schizophrenia), and he has become heavily programmed and conditioned to act the way he does. People with autism often show a lot of improvement in non-autistic areas, but one does not expect complete transformations.

SOME EFFECTS OF ANXIETY AND SHUTTING OUT

A child with autism exhibits behaviour which seems strange and puzzling to the majority of people. This will have resulted, in part, from partial or total shutdown or shutting out of emotion, sensation, and hence information. Let us consider some ways in which autism could be shaped by shutting-out behaviour and anxiety.

Lack of Social Awareness and Impairment of Relationships

If a degree of programmed shutdown fashions a child's general state, with an avoidance of emotion and adherence to certain rules, he may remain quite unaware of the needs of others and the rules by which they themselves live; it is a form of regimentation and of voluntary and involuntary withdrawal which is likely to have obsessional features. The child thinks in a singular, unimaginative way which is programmed, resistant to change and hard for him to alter, should he wish to. Hence his language may well be one-sided, as he talks *at* his listener rather than with him, and he may have profound difficulties in processing and linking ideas. His poor ability to understand may well extend to gestures and facial expressions; a knowing wink or look of resignation may even perplex an older child of good intelligence.

So the child who has autism is selective in his manner of listening and observing, making sense of what he hears and sees according to his own fixed criteria, rules, compulsive behaviour and ability to process information. If these restrictions prevent him from seeing things from another's point of view, there is nothing to stop him from indulging his obsessions and talking incessantly on one particular topic. He is unaware that he sounds too formal or pedantic as he copies the manner of speech of his teacher, and he is unaware that he is boring his listener or that he is being too familiar with someone. Maybe it is part of his ritualised behaviour to speak with a monotonous tone or maybe he does so because he has never processed the meaning of vocal intonation. Perhaps he is upset because people bully him or do not co-operate with him – but he is prevented from being able to understand why they respond to him in an unfavourable way. When one attempts to correct his behaviour he may, if his compulsive feelings permit, be able to alter it (perhaps by accepting a new rule or role), but any such alteration might not be brought about through empathy.

What may seem to be inappropriate laughing and giggling may be the result of some private thought, fear, heightened emotion or delayed or partial processing. It might also be an avoidance tactic in less severely affected children. Whatever the reason, such behaviour does nothing to enhance social relationships. Poor eye contact, restricted facial expression and staring blankly or through someone also hinder social communication, as does a restricted ability to understand humour – sarcasm, irony and metaphors are likely to be lost on the youngster, although some simple, obvious jokes may be really enjoyed.

Adherence to rules, restricted ability to process and connect ideas, and an absence of social awareness can make the child seem insensitive, or perhaps even callous. He is less able to exercise tact, speaking the literal truth and at inappropriate times. His sense of reality may be poor and his conscience underdeveloped.

It may be the case, however, that the child is not so affected by autism that he greatly lacks empathy with others. He may dislike himself for boring people with his inflexible conversation, for instance, but obsession and compulsion prevent him from doing otherwise.

Speech and Language

As well as the difficulties mentioned above, all the other speech and language problems described in Chapter Four can and do feature in the various shades of autism. In severe cases there may be so much withdrawal and negative conditioning that there is no verbal communication at all but these cases are in a minority.

THE CASE OF L.S. LOWRY

It is often helpful, when one wishes to understand a condition, to view it in one of its much less severe forms. Thanks to Tilly Marshall, I believe we can learn a lot from the case of L.S. Lowry. Tilly Marshall operated an art gallery in Newcastle upon Tyne and intimately knew the famous artist during the last fourteen years of his life. She wrote, "I wondered, as I often did, why we put up with his behaviour, but answered my own question, as ever, with the supposition that Lowry was almost certainly a man who had autistic symptoms." The account which I shall now give is based on her book, *Life with Lowry*.

As a boy Lowry had chopped up his mother's sideboard for no apparent reason and loved playing with little figures. When Tilly and Micky Marshall met him in 1960 he was already seventy-three years old. He was a tall, gangling man with sparkling blue eyes and short-cropped hair. His suit tended to be food-spotted, he wore an old, shabby raincoat and battered trilby and he lived in primitive conditions at home. Although he was such a talented artist there may have been some general awkwardness which might not be accounted for solely by his age. The author was to remark that he was no stranger to heavy falls, often tumbling on stairways; yet he showed remarkable physical resistance to any damage from them and would permit no attention after them.

Lowry had the ability to infuriate people but he was also able to move them to pity and to feel affection for him. Tilly Marshall refers to the "eternal child" in him. He, on the other hand, did not often consider the feelings of others; nor had he formed close family relationships.

Though a painter, he did not tend to show an appreciation of beautiful things. It occurred to Tilly Marshall that "...this was a strange man indeed who could feel no inner stirring at the beauty around him."

The artist sometimes withdrew from people, having the ability to put a barrier around himself whenever he wished. He might suddenly disappear and be found standing alone, leaning slightly sideways and backwards upon his walking-stick in total mental isolation. On other occasions he would feign sleep, yet be aware of conversations taking place.

Lowry always had a preference for the familiar and he disliked change. He liked to keep going to the same restaurant and to keep eating the same things. He was repetitive in his art and he would recount the same stories again and again. The writer tells us that everything Lowry had to say she and her companions had heard so often before. He always told the press the same things and he always began the day by talking about his imminent death, in spite of his good health. Lowry not only repeated himself; he encouraged others to repeat themselves.

He was prone to fidgeting, nervousness and apprehension in unfamiliar company and the Marshalls noticed that he exuded an unpleasant odour when he became unduly excited. He would "umm" and "aah" and mutter glumly when he was ill at ease with relative strangers and would need to go to the toilet more frequently – just as he did on a car journey when it was impossible to stop. Although he enjoyed an outing in the car, he had a habit of asking what would happen if a wheel fell off.

Lowry was obsessed with money and maintained, erroneously, that everyone wanted something from him for nothing. He was habitually mean, except with young girls whom he favoured; indeed, he became obsessed with one of them for a period of time. He liked to spend time gazing at young women and at clad and disrobed models in shop windows. His other obsessions were with the down-and-outs and with his own death. He repeatedly discussed his funeral in great detail: "...whenever life was a little dull he would cheer himself up by going through the routine for the umpteenth time and never omitted to assure us with a mischievous smile, 'I'll be there of course – but unfortunately only in a passive capacity.'"

When he was in an ill-mannered mood the artist could be "bored and boring" but he also had a tendency to fly into sudden and terrible rages for no apparent reason and without warning, losing control to the extent of becoming incontinent. Sometimes the reason for his anger was obvious: "In place of his favoured white tablecloth, there were the unaccustomed table mats. Lowry eyed these with an evil glint, and his mat eventually ended up under his feet. Despite instructions, the old man was served with sprouts. Quickly he pushed them off with his fork all over the table while I tried to scoop them up. Then he announced that it was ludicrous, simply fiendish (always a favourite word of disapproval), the table was far too close to him, and he did his utmost to push it over."

Lowry's problems constantly made him appear very selfish. Tilly Marshall had always to be on guard against his irritabilities which could spring up with no warning. She writes, "Once Lowry had decided that cold beef was the thing to eat he would glower and sulk if we looked at the menu...it was easier to suffer the cold beef than a Lowry temperament." Lowry always sat in the front of the Marshall's car and would never allow a window to be lowered, although his fellow passengers might stifle and the driver have to fight off drowsiness. He would persuade Tilly Marshall to entertain him on occasions when he knew she was overtired and wanted to return home to bed. He even dented the Marshall's new Volvo with his stick when their son, Simon, having taken him on a visit to Scotland, decided against taking the car over to Ireland with them to cut down on expenses. (The Marshalls naturally always paid.)

Lowry had an abhorrence of noise and background music. When a young, blind pianist began to play gently in a restaurant, the painter made such a commotion that the musician had to be asked to take a supper break. Tilly Marshall noticed that Lowry enjoyed observing tension in others. It seemed to her that he liked creating bizarre situations to sit back and observe how people coped with them. It appeared that he might indeed have been *able* to put up with the pianist's music during the incident (even bearing in mind any hypersensitivity), for when the young man eventually resumed his playing, the painter could not be persuaded that it was time to leave the restaurant and he sat for a further hour relatively unperturbed. (It may be that he was indulging in ritualistic behaviour, enjoying and needing to see a particular pattern of events unfolding.)

Many times over the years Tilly Marshall was to wonder at Lowry's preoccupation with his own affairs to the apparent exclusion of any compassion for others. She states that he had a sadistic streak within his character. He admitted that his pictures showing crippled people, bearded ladies and the suffering and disabilities of others were made without compassion. His love of creating difficult situations for the purpose of observing the results was a continuous enjoyment and amusement to him. He liked to see people suffer and frequently laughed at the misfortunes of others. In former years he had been a rent collector and had evicted people.

Lowry privately painted pictures of young girls in agony and torture, some decapitated by knife, sword, axe or guillotine – blood flowing, hands tied and chained, the male executioner represented only by the presence of the hand that wields the weapon. He was appalled, and at the same time fascinated, by the case of the Moors murders. He claimed that he attended the trial and he liked to discuss the particular plight of the young girl who called on God to help her in the agony of torture resulting in her death. He enjoyed standing outside the house where the crimes had taken place.

The painter had a fascination for young girls; indeed he made one his heir. But Tilly Marshall did not see Lowry as a man on his way to becoming a psychopath with paedophilic leanings, and she is likely to have been right. He did not appear to have a well-developed conscience (he told lies, for example), but he did abide by certain rules and was upset when these were not followed. Simon Marshall was about to move into a flat and he drove

Lowry to see it. Lowry panicked at the sight of a notice which read, 'Private Beyond Here', and objected to going any further because it was not allowed. I think this shows that one of Lowry's rules was to be law-abiding. (One cannot help wondering whether violent, pornographic and paedophilic videos have the power to weaken such a rule when they feed an obsession.)

Lowry had an alert mind, knew a great deal about other artists and their work, and was very observant of things which interested him; he remembered routes he had travelled along very well. He was an exact, punctual person who loathed being taken unawares by the press.

Another Side

In the words of Tilly Marshall, Lowry was "a man of parts". He was *capable* of experiencing normal emotions. He was, in fact, capable of feeling and caring for others. He told of feelings of love for a young girl whom he had favoured, he seemed able to consider the feelings of another young girl whom he had made his heir, and on one occasion he tried to comfort Tilly Marshall when she was in an overwrought state. On a further occasion, on an impulse, he wanted her to accept two little paintings to which he was attached, as a birthday present. (This was quite out of character, since Lowry was generally very mean.) He often liked to receive attention and affection, although he loathed people to be obsequious. He not only knew how to behave very well and to keep his mood controlled before people who were not close friends – he was sometimes able to modify his behaviour if he were criticised.

Describing Lowry's paintings of moorland, Tilly Marshall writes, "His breast-shaped hills stand out against a grey sky and convey a feeling of natural majesty, basically repelling to any comfort-seeking observer. Like Lowry's seascapes, they are uncompromising, uncomfortable but utterly authoritative – almost abstract painting, and the greatest example of Lowry's primordial sense of loneliness. The more popular and better known mill scenes did not portray the same innermost Lowry." He was obviously a man who was capable of experiencing deep feelings. One day he even remarked on the beauty of a flower arrangement.

It was not difficult to hurt Lowry's feelings with tactless comments or by slighting his work, although he was modest about his paintings. He seemed capable, too, of feeling ashamed; he did not want people to know, for example, that he had once been evicted because he had let a house become filthy and run-down, and he did not want people to see his erotic paintings, although he was happy for them to view his other works. It may well be the case that he realised that his obsessions and rituals were tiresome for others and although he may have derived some satisfaction from being unpleasant, he may have disliked himself for his behaviour. One day, when in a happy, relaxed state, he admitted, "I'm not at all a nice man."

The artist seemed capable of both experiencing jealousy himself and recognising it in others. He also had the wherewithal to be devious. He could be clever with words and fun loving (even engaging in some repartee), and he was able to see absurdities in situations. And importantly, he was able to use imagination: during his model gazing episodes his imagination wove endless stories around the dummies.

Lowry had the capacity to be critical of others' bad behaviour and he hated violence, mugging and terrorism.

Conclusion

Milder degrees of behaviour seen in autism are frequently described as eccentric 'artistic temperament'. It is true that Lowry's social relationships were not grossly impaired but they were significantly hampered due to problems found in autism. We can see that along with his condition there were all the normal human feelings but that these were often prevented from surfacing by obsessive, ritualistic behaviour, selective attention, avoidance and withdrawal. In other words, they are prevented from surfacing by normal childhood personality traits which exist to a greater degree than is usual. Features of autism and normality frequently co-exist. It is most reasonable to consider the possibility that behind every case of autism lies a person who is prevented from thinking and behaving normally, by entrenched traits which can be related to anxiety.

CHAPTER NINE

ANXIETY AND MENTAL STATES

EXTRAORDINARY ABILITY AND DIFFERENT STATES OF CONSCIOUSNESS

It appears to be the case that withdrawing the mind from the external world might favour the production of extraordinary ability and even what we choose to call psychic phenomena, or psi. Concentrating, relaxing and stilling the mind (with consequent low levels of cortical arousal) seems to help people to carry out extraordinary or spectacular physical feats or to withstand extremes of temperature (as in fire walking).

This excluding behaviour, or concentrating of the mind or using it in a different way which may involve a different belief system, appears to help some regular meditators to dramatically alter the way their bodies function. American cardiologist Herbert Benson and colleagues (1982) attached electronic measuring devices to three Tibetan monks practising g Tum-mo yoga. He found that finger and toe temperature could be raised by as much as 7.2 and 8.3 degrees Celsius, respectively.

Unusual phenomena may also be encouraged through other activities which concentrate the mind, such as can occur in the martial arts.

It may be that the extraordinary abilities and functioning of some children who withdraw are likewise associated with a different state of consciousness. We are still largely ignorant in matters of psi phenomena and T. McMullen (1991) questions the validity of D.A. Treffert's evidence that extrasensory perception occurs in certain autistic savant children. We do know, however, that emotion can be expressed at an unconscious level through the autonomic nervous system. It can stimulate action in the sympathetic and parasympathetic nerves which serve the entire body and regulate its functions. We know that this overactivity of the autonomic system is responsible for our panic attacks and psychosomatic symptoms and diseases. Although many parts of the autonomic nervous system are able to function on a spinal basis, its activity is normally under the control of centres in the medulla, hypothalamus and cerebral cortex.

It is of interest, therefore, when considering the symptoms of children who are anxious or who have shut down responses, that the hypothalamus appears to be important in the regulation of temperature (some children throw up high body temperatures for no apparent reason), appetite and thirst, and controls the release of the pituitary hormones – which include the growth hormone (some of the children are very small and underweight). The hypothalamus appears to be a link between the central and autonomic nervous systems and between the nervous system and the endocrine glands. Adzhimolaev and colleagues have found that changes in autonomic function during emotional stress may lead to marked disturbances of homeostasis, and in particular, of temperature regulation (Adzhimolaev et al., 1989).

MENTAL ILLNESS

It has been noted above that emotional disquiet can result in disorder at a host of sites throughout the body; sometimes the brain itself is the site and mental illness ensues.

Mental illness is common. It is much more prevalent than many people suppose, the stigma associated with it resulting in it being less often discussed, or complained of, than most other illnesses. No physical cause can be shown in the majority of cases. Were it generally appreciated that a large proportion of young children have high levels of anxiety, the prevalence of mental illness would not seem so surprising.

I have already alluded to family units where symptoms associated with anxiety or tension take a variety of forms – one member may be obsessional, one dyslexic, one hyperactive and another depressed, for example. Over the years, I have known several boys with autism who each have a father and/or brother with dyslexia, and Bailey and colleagues (1995) highlight the fact that several different research groups have found an elevated rate of cognitive (including speech and language) abnormalities and social deviations in the first-degree relatives of autistic individuals. Although I have not made it part of my enquiry to ask about the mental health of a child's close relatives, I have personally come across a boy with autism who had an older schizophrenic sister; many children with hyperactivity, autism, speech and language difficulties or dyslexia who each have a parent or close relative suffering from depression, manic-depressive illness or an anxiety state; a hyperactive child with a very depressed sibling; and fraternal twins where one suffered from depression and another from schizophrenia.

More able people with autism are believed to be particularly at risk of developing depression or an anxiety state, especially during adolescence and early adulthood. They also appear to be more vulnerable to psychosis than people without autism. Wolff and Chick (1980) have drawn attention to schizophrenia in this context, and Gillberg (1985) and Wing (1981) have highlighted manic-depressive or depressive illness. People with autism respond to conventional drug treatment for mania, depression and schizophrenia, in the same way as people without autism.

Depression

The initial symptoms of depression might be seen as a slowing down and shutting off by the body and mind – often mixed with symptoms of stress. Symptoms of depression and stress might seem to counterbalance one another, the former signalling low arousal, whilst stress symptoms suggest a highly aroused state.

When a person needs rest, such as after a bout of influenza, a stressful time or a highly stimulating or exhilarating and perhaps sleep-deprived period, it may be to his advantage to slow down, lose some of his former enthusiasm for doing things, sleep more, feel less capable and perhaps experience some emotional numbness. In the extreme, however, these characteristics form melancholia or depression.

Depression is a very common illness, but some people are more prone to it than others. What causes this vulnerability? Quite high levels of tension or anxiety seem to be an important factor. These are particularly likely to be present in the fearful person or worrier, in someone who lacks confidence and is highly sensitive to criticism, and in the exacting, methodical, industrious and often highly popular and successful person. Those who are very witty, jolly and lively may have a tendency towards misery and be more susceptible to depression; again we seem to have a counterbalancing effect.

The teenager, with his heightened emotions, can be vulnerable to an initial attack. (It is even conceivable that conditioned reactions or learned responses resulting from a first bout might make him more vulnerable to a future attack, perhaps enabling depression to recur without the same degree of provocation which was necessary initially.) It is important that we should be alert to the condition of a young person who seems particularly prone to lethargy, rather than dismiss it as normal teenage behaviour. We should also be alert to the various degrees of depression when considering children at any stage of childhood.

Depression in Childhood

In a review of the literature demonstrating the existence of prepubertal and adolescent depression, Angold (1988) notes that the full range of adult depressive symptoms may be expressed by children by the age of six years. It is important to note symptoms associated with depression which are commonly found in children, even though there may be a different cause:

- tiredness and lethargy
- apathy
- loss of appetite
- sleep disturbances
- pessimism
- lack of confidence and self-worth
- fear
- weepiness
- lack of concentration and problems with memory
- withdrawal
- lack of affection
- irritability
- anger
- school avoidance

The risk of depression might be increased if a youngster's learning difficulties have not been understood by himself and others. Even if his difficulties have not been entirely remedied, he is likely to feel more confident if they are not a mystery to him.

Schizophrenia

Early Behaviour of People who became Schizophrenic

In 1986 two Frenchmen, J.J. Etchepare and M. Bourgeois, compared the early behaviour of thirty-five adults suffering from schizophrenia with thirty-five controls. The information was gained by questioning parents and the results are shown in the following table:

0 – 5 years

	Schizophrenics	Controls
Sleeping difficulties	15	8
Feeding difficulties	14	7
Bodily Ailments	12	11
Lack of bladder control	12	2
Behavioural problems	14	5
Very good and docile children	11	2
Treatment for nervousness or insomnia	7	2
Very shy	6	3
Hospitalised during early childhood	3	9
Serious organic illness	4	3
Perinatal difficulties	3	3
Walking difficulties	1	1
Fears and phobias	2	2
Delayed language	2	2

6 – 12 years

	Schizophrenics	Controls
Poor performance at school	17	11
Withdrawal/isolation	17	1
Phobic/obsessional	12	5
Lack of bladder control	10	2
Dreamy	8	1
Anxious	6	0
Aggressive	7	4
Bizarre behaviour/ideas	6	1
Excessive shyness	6	0
Repeated complaints of aches and pains	6	3
Organic illnesses	4	9
Sleeping difficulties	4	2

It can be seen that, in this study, problems which can be associated with anxiety tended to be more common in the children who went on to develop schizophrenia.

THE CASE OF CAROL NORTH, M.D.

In her book entitled *Welcome, Silence* Carol North describes her experiences as a severely affected schizophrenic and the way she became cured and able to qualify as a psychiatrist. The reader might compare some of her personality traits with those commonly occurring in other young children (Chapter Three).

Carol North was an American child who was small for her age. When she was a baby she was hospitalised several times for diarrhoea and dehydration. At the age of four she had a fever with a temperature of one hundred and six and a half degrees. The cause was never discovered and it departed as mysteriously as it had come. When Carol was six years old her mother remarked that the child's appetite had never been very good and that she still had a lot of stomachaches. Mrs. North told a psychologist that her daughter could not stand the texture of pulp in orange juice, nor tolerate her socks falling down or her underwear creeping up. It was necessary to be careful what was said in Carol's presence because she was apt to misinterpret it. She was taken to the psychologist because she had become alarmingly frightened after discovering a very severe fire in her home one Saturday. As a result of the fire she could not bear to be alone and could not sleep in her own bed. She stayed awake all night keeping watch, in case the fire returned, feeling that her mother and father did not appreciate the gravity of the situation.

During the night following the fire Carol's visual perception became disturbed. Seeing her terror, her father encouraged her to come to him, but Carol found that a hundred or so 'Popeye arms' had materialised out of the air between herself and her father, blocking her path to safety.

The author states that she was terrified at the idea of being alone in her room long enough to get dressed, in case she was trapped by the Popeye arms and burned alive when the fire came back. She feigned sleep to please her parents but as she lay in bed she heard men's voices, although there were no men. After seeing a ghost, the child felt something crawl up her leg and saw hordes of bugs swarming all over her pillow.

Following the fire Carol North sensed danger on her walks to school. She explains how at six years old she was afraid of everything and began sleeping in her parents' bed regularly.

Unfortunately, the psychologist's diagnosis on the visit to him three months after the fire was that the young Carol North was seeking attention. It did not occur to the child that other people did not hear voices; she believed that it was just wrong to talk about them. Carol learned to hide her fear, no matter how frightening things became. She continued to hope that when she became grown up she would not be scared and would no longer have to pretend. Meanwhile, she devised strategies for covering up and coping with her fears; she even played the piano as loudly as she could to drown the voices.

Carol became aware of coloured patterns which decorated the air. She had actually been seeing them for some time but had never paid attention to them; she believed that everyone saw them and that they were a visual equivalent to background noise. "These patterns, composed of tiny spicules and multicoloured squiggly lines, wiggled and wormed their way around and through each other like people milling in a crowd." She called them 'Interference Patterns'. At times they intensified, sweeping across the front of her eyes, affecting everything she looked at. A sneeze or a door slamming might release an explosion of associated designs and colours into the air so that she was actually 'seeing sounds'.

In class, Carol experienced obsessional thoughts and her eyes would lock into a comfortable stare as she drifted off for hours. She claims that this behaviour became so habitual that it resulted in her staring at people.

As a teenager, Carol found that her thoughts thinned out so much that she could find nothing to say. She writes, "Meanwhile, my perceptions magnified. My mind, a vacuum, slipped into a state of Pure Perception; environmental stimuli constantly bombarded my senses with unrelenting, nearly unbearable intensity. The rustling of a book's page turning produced paroxysms of Interference Patterns materialising out of the air, capturing my total awareness."

In spite of her problems and difficulty concentrating in class, Carol achieved well academically. Nonetheless, she lacked confidence in her very ample abilities, always feeling that she needed to work harder than everyone else. She was very strongly motivated to work and a punctual and dependable person. She left school and went to college.

The evergreens around the college campus appeared to Carol to have burst into very intense contrasts of colour. Like the fire in her childhood, the sights were so intense that they were both horrible and beautiful at the same time. Feeling weighed down with the 'burden' of Pure Perception, she spent hours scrutinising textures and patterns and believed they held special messages for her. Her boyfriend kept finding her staring at a wall, not moving a muscle. He became concerned when she would not answer him; she delighted in the belief that her voices were answering for her. She discovered that when she was physically fatigued and stressed, particularly around examination times, she was most susceptible to her hallucinatory voices.

The student was admitted to a psychiatric hospital as a hopeless case of catatonic schizophrenia. She explains how she stood motionless for hours in strange postures for, what seemed to her, logical, altruistic reasons and she was able to free her body from tight hospital restraints. She was frightened, expressionless, paranoid, and obsessional. She had strange sensations and she tried to cut open her foot to see machines inside it. She had panic attacks, out-of-the-body experiences, found herself talking in a strange voice, and she walked stiffly. Even as a very young child she had had difficulty understanding other people's facial expressions; now her visual distortions resulted in her finding that a doctor's expression alternated between a grin and a frown at the speed of about four times per second. Sometimes she felt so inert that when she tried to smile her face felt dead; sometimes she smiled at her voices.

She withdrew and time passed without her having awareness of it; inside her emotion felt flat and vacant. In her own words, *"I withdrew from the world, allowing myself to drift with the interference, relaxing from the awful strain of trying to stay functional the rest of the time."*

Schizophrenia and Autism

The symptoms of schizophrenia can sometimes be seen in other conditions, perhaps in a milder form. Delusions and hallucinations can occur in severe depression, for example. When comparing autism with schizophrenia we are in the one case considering a person who has possibly always seemed to behave abnormally, and in the other the person's behaviour has undergone great change from a comparatively normal state. Certainly somebody who develops schizophrenia generally has a lot more experience of thinking and behaving normally. There are, for instance, some pertinent speech and language differences. Having had richer experiences of life and not having previously restricted his thinking, the dissociated person with schizophrenic symptoms is better able to indulge in jumbled fantasies and speak in puns and riddles, strange though these might seem. Further, the child with autism is likely to lack potential for sophisticated paranoia, unlike the person with schizophrenia who has understood the ways of the world better.

Nevertheless, there are many features which may exist with both autism and poor mental health. We see children with autism watching their fingers or some objects intently, perhaps while they move them repetitively. At such times they appear switched off to the rest of the world. I have known children with autism who like to scrutinise the hairs on the back of people's necks. Are they indulging in the same 'Pure Perception' as Carol North experienced? (Children with autism may shut their eyes at the same time as they are reacting to a sound. Might they be, in some instances, 'seeing the sneezes' as did Carol North, rather than necessarily be trying to block out everything or confusing their senses?) North writes of her thoughts thinning out and disappearing. Without awareness of time or emotion she 'drifted' with the interference. *In Autism: An Inside-Out Approach* Donna Williams describes a similar experience – the hypnotic pull of a world where there is no mind or 'I' and no imagination. Her world can exist at different levels – some easier to be called back from than others.

In both schizophrenia and autism it is extremely difficult to make an emotional impact on the person. People with schizophrenia may hold odd postures, walk stiffly or idiosyncratically and harm their own bodies, as might someone suffering from autism. Indeed, the two conditions can share many of the personality traits described in Chapters Two, Three and Four.

Some anxious infants may develop in an autistic way. Some other children might develop relatively normally, coping with immoderate anxieties or acquiring them a little later once normal patterns of behaviour have been learned. These youngsters might be at risk of mental illness later in life, perhaps during particularly stressful stages, such as their passage into adulthood. They would not be protected in the way that a child displaying a marked degree of autism is protected, through his withdrawal. This would explain why more able people with autism seem particularly vulnerable to mental illness.

In the case of Carol North, an inability to read facial expressions well and the fact that her parents had to be careful what they said to her in case she misinterpreted it, may be indicative of some autistic-type withdrawal and rigidity of thought but she had learned normal behaviour patterns and it appears that she wore her anxiety more on her sleeve. Had she been protected by more autistic-type behaviour, she might never have experienced schizophrenia – but she is unlikely to have become a psychiatrist.

One could indeed hypothesise that children with autism have safeguarded themselves to varying degrees against mental illness, whilst the less protected highly anxious child is more at risk, particularly during the vulnerable adolescent years. If this is so, an overlap, medley and divergence of symptoms are all to be expected. We can see just such an overlap in the childhood symptoms of Carol North and Donna Williams. In her book, *Nobody Nowhere,* Williams describes how, frightened of going to sleep, she would sleep with her eyes open, and how feeling safe was a tiring business. Her protection was through wisps or tiny creatures which hung in the air above her, along with tiny spots (air particles) which became a hypnotic foreground to a faded out world. Williams was able to brave 'the world' by assuming particular characters. This helped her to develop her intellect and ability to communicate, whilst retaining protection when it was needed through an escape into her own world (having learned to lose herself in patterns and sounds). Carol North, on the other hand, remained terrified throughout the night, stayed awake to keep guard, hallucinated and became deluded. She had not initially taught herself how to relax with the patterns which she saw decorating the air and she had already become too much a part of the real world. Her degree of withdrawal was insufficient as a protection against evils and her mind lost touch with the world in another manner – she became deluded.

Donna Williams, however, has not been totally protected against mental illness. She did succumb on occasions to depression as she battled in the world. And during her later childhood she did hallucinate in a state of fatigue – because nightmares (which included sleepwalking) had made her terrified to fall asleep.

If we continue to use terms such as autism and schizophrenia, then of course we must continue to make a distinction between childhood schizophrenia and autism. Autism is evident very early in life and prevents the child from learning how to think and behave normally. Even in children in the Asperger category some abnormal behaviour is heavily programmed in the brain and a resistance to change must contribute to keeping the behaviour patterns in some measure. Were autism to be known as childhood schizophrenia, there might be the risk that the child would be given inappropriate treatment. It is important to be very aware of each youngster's particular symptoms.

Obsessive-Compulsive Behaviour

Obsessive-compulsive thinking and behaviour is increased by stress. As it is common in children, and since it can become a mental illness and be responsible for much criminal activity in children and adults, reduction or redirection of tension should perhaps be a top priority in our society.

There is the particular problem of people becoming addicted to certain kinds of excitement, which is a form of compulsive behaviour. Many people enjoy the 'highs' or 'buzzes' they obtain from taking risks and we see an instance of this in the popularity of joyriding among youths. Sufferers of bulimia nervosa may find that the buzz and relief after they have vomited and purged themselves are addictive. There is too, the child who confronts his fears (perhaps of death and violence) and becomes fascinated and obsessed with them.

Some people are compulsively helpful towards others to the neglect of themselves. Then there are the compulsive shoppers who obtain highs from their purchasing. Indeed, any kind of behaviour may become compulsive.

***

The mental health of children is rarely considered until something goes wrong. And when things do go wrong, perhaps in the teenage years, we are so often astonished, for we had failed to see that the youngster was at risk. It would seem to be a somewhat neglected area.

I have tried to show on previous pages that fears in childhood are not only commonplace but often marked; there does not always seem to be a strong provocation for them, such as the fire in Carol North's case. The child, Jude, whose problems I outlined in Chapter Four (p.60) displays fears of a worrying level, and the behaviour of many other children whom I have seen might make us more vigilant concerning their present and future mental health (for example, Joe, p.66). There is perhaps a case for broadening preschool and school medicals to enquire into the child's personality in some depth. There would, of course, be no need to alarm parents, but helping them to better understand their child's behaviour can only be a step in the right direction, whether one is concerned for the youngster's mental health or for his learning ability.

CHAPTER TEN

HELPING THE CHILD AFTER ENQUIRING INTO HIS PERSONALITY TRAITS

"A mind that wishes to understand a problem must not only understand the problem completely, wholly, but must be able to follow it swiftly, because the problem is never static."
J. Krishnamurti (1895-1986)

When we make our own judgements with an open mind which is not limited to theories, current opinions and often heard but ill-considered or inappropriate advice, we are more likely to act in the best interests of a child for that particular moment. Hence lists of 'what to do' and 'what not to do' might be at best unhelpful and at worst, harmful. Each child is highly individual and circumstances vary. Of course it is wise to take note of possible methods or courses of action but we should only employ them when we are fully aware of the child's needs. Many appropriate actions come not as the result of pre-planned programmes but intuitively, while talking or working with a child, as long as there is an understanding of his feelings. When there is no real understanding of his feelings he will, no doubt, sense it, just as he senses when we are too anxious that he should make progress. As a general rule, our interactions with him should be an enjoyable experience for him and for ourselves. The results then boost not only his confidence, but also our own.

Understanding a child after an investigation into his personality traits would enable us to better gauge the amount and type of pressure he can cope with and hence reduce the risk of us unwittingly increasing compulsive avoidance behaviour, other compulsive behaviour and switching off. We might discover that for one particular child the local nursery is too high-powered and that a more relaxed playgroup would be preferable, whereas for another, the local nursery gives a more structured routine with which he can more easily relax. We may become aware that abrupt commands or critical comments are adversely affecting a sensitive youngster, that a hyperactive child needs a more stimulating lesson to hold his attention or that a child who is hypersensitive to sound should be in a quieter room. We might discover, too, that a child is feeling more tense or anxious than usual and we may find that we can reduce his troubles. We may see that a state of selective withdrawal is masking some anxiety.

FURTHER SUGGESTIONS

Some specific ideas for helping a sensitive child have been given in previous chapters. They include breaking down tasks for children who are conditioned to switch off, panic or become flustered, giving nondidactic help with reading and writing to prevent or remove literacy problems, and giving, to a child who works slowly, time goals for very small items of work which are well within his capability, in a relaxed setting (Chapter Six). Some ideas for helping children with speech and language difficulties are included in Chapter Four. The following list offers some further suggestions which might be applicable when considering a child's welfare:

A.   He may be better left to explore some equipment which is new to him; he may need time to familiarise himself with it in a relaxed way before an adult begins to give explanations or instructions.

B.   He may benefit from being told exactly what is planned for a session, morning, afternoon, or even for a week or more. He may like to know how long he is going to spend on a particular task at school. He may like to have such information written down or illustrated.

C.   It may be better if he does not see how quickly and easily an adult can perform a task, or is not told how easy it is to accomplish.

D.   He may benefit from receiving very precise explanations or directions, stated slowly, clearly and unemotionally, with adequate pausing and avoiding an overload of information.

E.   Concepts such as colours and prepositions may be better taught naturally in a relaxed manner, rather than didactically. One might, for example, encourage him whilst he is playing to put "this red brick" on top of a tower of bricks rather than tell him that a certain brick is red, or ask him what colour it is or if he can find a red one.

F.   It may be prudent to ensure that new activities do not replace repetition with games, books, etc., where an infant or young child responds well to it.

G.   It may be advisable to maintain an awareness of how much one is doing for the child, rather than with him.

H.   He may benefit from being asked, "How would you like me to help you?"

I.   It may be expedient that he is not present at a case conference or other meeting or gathering where his level and achievements are being discussed, even when he seems to comprehend very poorly. On the other hand, he may benefit from being party to a constructive and sensitive discussion of his personality traits involving a parent and a single professional. He may like to hear his fears and little habits aired without criticism. (I have generally found that children, after listening and perhaps even contributing to such a discussion while they play, leave the room in a cheerful mood. I have had a case where a young child's literacy difficulties cleared up afterwards with no remedial activities whatsoever. Furthermore, a period of discussion while the child plays, if he wishes to, enables him to grow properly accustomed to the room and speech and language therapist or other professional so that he tends to respond more favourably to demands made upon him later.)

J.   If his age is appropriate, he may benefit from having his learning difficulties properly explained to him.

K.   If he switches off in a group situation, he may benefit from being addressed with one other child, then with two, and so on, until he is accustomed to listening in a larger group – whereas keeping him in a larger group might result in reinforcement of the negative behaviour. On the other hand, there is the child who, in seeking to avoid emotional involvement or demands, fails to attend when he is addressed on an individual level but sometimes listens well in a group situation – one might try gradually reducing the group's number.

L.   It may be advisable to help him, in a non-critical way, to keep his conversation on track – at the first sign of his wandering off it.

M.   He may benefit from being given help to gain insight with regard to the effects of his behaviour and the feelings of others. He might be asked, calmly and simply, why someone is angry or upset as the result of his actions.

N.   If he has obsessions, rituals or special but no general interests, these might be turned to advantage; they could be used as a starting point from which to broaden his learning. If he is very young and not involving himself at all in the world but has a strong liking for, let us say, a certain food, it might be possible to repetitively reward him with the food item for co-operating in any very simple action or activity (physical contact may be necessary to prompt). This could help to desensitise him to demands, so that he relinquishes some control.

O.   If he withdraws and avoids contact or demands one might refrain from responding to him with an overbearing vivacity and respect a possible need he may have to observe things calmly, indirectly or even peripherally. One might keep involvement and physical contact to a minimum, on his own terms, seeking to increase his involvement very gradually – perhaps by making a slightly personal demand, nonchalantly and within a safe, structured, predictable setting. He may even fare better without praise, and if he is not necessarily expected to comply with social etiquette.

P. If he is responding poorly to conversation or demands, tactics might be subtly changed at once to avoid reinforcement of negative behaviour.

Q. If he is mute, except for some sounds, and if he enjoys noting, and perhaps controlling, cause and effect, he may like to hear an adult echoing his sounds. This may encourage him to experiment with sounds and help to desensitise him with regard to his mutism, but one must beware of taking early liberties and attempting to transform his sounds into meaningful words. However, he may enjoy having his sound transformed into an Indian war cry by the action of an adult's hand or hearing it altered by a gentle tapping against his chest. A form of alternative communication might help some mute or speech-impoverished children; for example, picture board, sign language or electronic machine.

R. If he is severely withdrawn and shows a wish to regress and return to infancy, he might benefit from being allowed to recapitulate his early years. He may involve himself a little more the second time round if we respond sympathetically.

S. He may benefit from being encouraged to channel anger or an excess of tension into a physical activity.

T. The child with autism sometimes masters the mechanics of reading with great speed but at the expense of attending to meaning. It may be advisable to attempt to restrain the reading process in the early stages while help is given to connect the words with meaning and context. (Obsessions might be utilised here, if necessary.)

U. If a child compartmentalises his world and this contributes to a reluctance to discuss school life at home, or vice versa, one might try, very gradually, to broaden his associations. A teacher might show him pictures of, and talk about, his or her *own* family life, rather than allow the child to view teachers as permanent fixtures of the school.

SOME OF THE AUTHOR'S INDIVIDUAL CASES

The purpose of this sample of cases is to show how an understanding of the personality traits of a child can help determine the way we treat his problems and behave towards him. It is not intended as a full description of the speech and language therapy carried out with the children, although in some cases none other was required. Nor do I mean to imply that all cases are remediable.

No single approach is the right one, except for a particular child at a particular time and perhaps with a particular person or in a particular place. Hence if we stick to a 'method', it will sometimes be wrong. Just as one child's traits can seem opposite to another's, so may appropriate approaches differ.

Sometimes a better understanding on the part of a parent is enough to get the ball rolling, as the following cases illustrate:

Moura

Moura's mother was suffering from mild depression. She knew she was good with other people's children but felt a degree of inadequacy in failing to draw desirable responses from her three-year-old daughter. Moura's short sentences were comprised of vowels and jargon with clear words occasionally intermingled. She avoided involvement, such as conversation, and had tended from birth to switch off, with the result that it could be difficult to obtain her attention and her understanding was inconsistent. She had severe temper tantrums in which she could be quite aggressive and destructive. She was easily frightened (yet displayed a poor sense of danger), was extremely alarmed by foggy weather and very sensitive to criticism; she had attacks of asthma. She was obsessed with bags and collecting little objects and she used words repetitively. She was ambidextrous and she had a squint. She was not toilet trained, had always slept restlessly and had established very particular eating habits. She had a surprisingly good memory for past events, worked a video recorder extremely competently, had a precise knowledge of routes to various places and displayed a liking for sameness. Her attention tended to flit from one thing to another. She was often very active and excitable but on the few occasions when she attempted to dress herself, she was slow and seemed unable to sequence or organise her actions.

Once Moura's mother had properly considered that her child's behaviour might be related to anxiety and tension which had been present in earliest infancy, she was less inclined to blame herself for all her daughter's problems and better able to react to them. She began to feel useful and purposeful and her energy revived. It would appear that Moura reacted favourably to a greater degree of routine, tolerance and calmness for, within a year, her symptoms had significantly abated and her jargon was largely replaced by clear speech. Her mother gave her precise explanations in a calm manner and her understanding developed.

Leon

It had been suggested to his mother that two-year-old Leon was profoundly deaf. He was always silent except during his pronounced temper tantrums and bouts of crying. It transpired that he had a whole host of very marked anxiety-related traits, and mutism and withdrawal was certainly an alternative diagnosis. Leon's mother began to acknowledge the extent of his fears and in the course of time the department of audiology was able to confirm that he had satisfactory hearing. His family stopped referring to him as being deaf and took more care over what was said in his presence. His reactions to all life's events were carefully noted and his fears were prevented as far as possible. Routine and his rituals were respected, as was his need to be aloof. Gradually he began to speak, but the family's watchfulness is necessarily ongoing.

George

Nowhere can understanding be more needed than with the Attention Deficit Hyperactivity Disorder. This label fitted nine-year-old George for he displayed all the usual manifestations. Acknowledging the tension associated with the problems enabled George's parents to stop nagging him; this was a desirable effect since he had begun to live up to his reputation as a hopeless but rather comical roguish lad, always fulfilling everyone's expectations – the openly acknowledged walking disaster. Instead of relying on constant correction of his poor attention to behaviour and speech, informative books were read and helpful strategies were adopted by the boy's parents. The tidying of George's room became a joint, relatively peaceful activity for him and his mother; no longer did she do it all herself after shouting instructions which were not properly adhered to. In other matters too, George was helped to organise his activities better. Tasks were broken down into smaller units which did not try his patience so easily and routine was respected. Praise was given whenever it was due and a calmer atmosphere reigned at home. Perfection was neither demanded nor its absence bemoaned.

Whilst George's parents were unable to control others' reactions to their son, they felt that a discussion with his school teachers was helpful. There can be little doubt that, although he did not lose his basic problematic traits, George became more relaxed and better able to manage them through his parents' approach, borne of an improved understanding. Perhaps aided by enhanced self-esteem, he began to attend better to the delivery of his speech.

Kim's school became much more actively involved:

Kim

Kim was a six-year-old who had difficulty attending in the classroom where she switched off, gave muddled, irrelevant answers to questions, showed recurring patterns of thought and did not tend to keep 'on track'. She had frequent nightmares and a strong liking for sameness. She had a tendency to walk backwards.

A good appreciation of Kim's difficulties was assisted by an outstanding effort made by her school. Her classroom teacher and a classroom assistant took turns to make detailed observations of her behaviour during some school sessions. Notes that were taken were later typed up and viewed in relationship to Kim's personality traits. They contributed greatly to her parents' and my own understanding as well as to that of the teacher and assistant. They highlighted in particular habitual switching off patterns of the child and the extent to which she was relying on copying her classmates in order to carry out activities. As a result, new classroom strategies were devised for helping Kim to concentrate on tasks and to attend to what was said. These included addressing her in a smaller group (using precise language with adequate pausing), breaking down tasks into very small parts (sometimes attaching a time limit), raising motivation by telling her exactly what was planned for a session, and avoiding criticism. Kim benefited from our shared enhanced sensitivity to her needs.

Whilst Andy's fortunes might not necessarily have been different had he had different early experiences, it may be that he would have benefited from greater sensitivity to his needs:

Andy

Andy's is not a success story. As an anxious three-year-old he regularly reorganised the furniture if it were not as he was accustomed to see it and he avoided eye contact and speaking. When he did speak he exhibited a lateral *s* and a squeaky voice, and he said the minimum he could. He refused to speak at his nursery where his anxiety may well have been increased by the teacher engaging in a battle of wills with him – unsuccessfully demanding speech of him and withdrawing privileges because he withheld it. Since there was no sign of this approach desensitising Andy, it perhaps ought to have been abandoned in favour of another. Appointments for speech and language therapy were not kept.

Andy ended his school days in a school for children with learning difficulties and difficult behaviour. He used obscene language, maintained his lateral *s* and had developed an eye twitching tic. His friends were frightened by the lengths to which he could go with his disobedience and aggression. He got into trouble with the police. He was dyslexic.

Varying degrees of a nonintrusive approach helped Ingrid, Julian and Scott:

Ingrid

This reticent, accident prone, thumb-sucking little girl of an immaculately dressed and spotless family attended the speech and language clinic at the age of four because of her delayed language; earlier appointments had been offered but never kept, for her parents had great difficulty remembering them. Her verbal comprehension, in a formal test situation, was delayed by more than a year. Her general responses were slow and her speech and language infantile. She tended to act silly, which wasted time and embarrassed her parents who lacked confidence in their ability to help or cope with her. Ingrid had been sent to the nursery class of a local private school to catch up with her peers before she became properly of school age but this seemed to have the reverse effect of that intended. She became further behind in relation to other children in her age group, became more repetitively disobedient, and was removed to a local playgroup.

Ingrid's parents were helped to consider the possible significance of her inactivity from early infancy, her sensitivity, her current restlessness, occasional bouts of rocking, her repetitive 'naughty' behaviour and weepiness on being left at school. They came to realise that her learning difficulties were more likely to be related to her tension and concerns rather than to inherent inability. Their own anxiety over her poor attainment was lessened as she began to improve, with a decrease in demands being made on her, a nondidactic approach, and possibly as the result of a less hectic lifestyle after her mother reduced her working hours. Therapy for Ingrid's immature articulation of words had been considered inappropriate, especially as she was generally understood by others. She did retain some of her early sound patterns but these were easily corrected at the age of six years when she was ready to relinquish them. Ingrid is now a happy seven-year-old whose confidence continues to grow and whose bouts of silliness continue to diminish. After some initial concerns about her inability to read, her teacher is happy with her progress in the area of literacy.

Julian

Julian is one of three children in a family where mild-moderate symptoms of autism, dyslexia and panic intermingle among its members, including the parents. His mother said that he had always switched off. At the age of three and a half years he lacked good eye contact, was mute except for an occasional word and he displayed an abnormal degree of sensitivity to, or awareness of, extraneous sounds. He was seen alone regularly in the speech and language clinic for nonintrusive therapy and proved psychologically ready to move forward.

Activities were carried out in a matter-of-fact way and pictures and stories were spoken about without eye contact, unwarranted animation, questioning, praise, or indeed, without reference to (or overt acknowledgement of) any participation by Julian. Whilst playing with some toy construction shapes, I even occasionally removed one from his possession, for my use, without the customary polite request. The first two sessions drew little response from the child but he was nevertheless interested in the activities and in what he was hearing. Then he began to participate in a relaxed and consistent manner and his speech developed with reasonable ease. His mother was delighted to tell of regular speaking at home. At four and three quarters Julian took up his place in a mainstream school and no problems were reported by his teachers a year later.

Julian was able to break his negative habits at the clinic partly because of the approach, but also because, being hitherto unknown to him, the room and I were not so much a part of his negative programming as his home and family had been.

Scott

Sleepwalking was commonplace among three-year-old Scott's family members and he too was prone to it. One day his mother brought him to the clinic with what she described as a worrying cough. When I responded to the rather empty, unconvincing cough by echoing it back to him he stopped, grinned, and experimented with it and my responses; it appeared to be the early stage of a tic.

Scott's mother was concerned that he seemed to be "on another planet". He had been an exemplary baby in terms of goodness but he developed attacks of arrested breathing and convulsions which became diagnosed as epilepsy. He had difficulty in appreciating that what happened yesterday did not necessarily take place every day. He was easily frightened, reticent, restless, and sought comforters and sameness. He was left-handed, visually inattentive, a little clumsy, somewhat switched off and tended to avoid demands.

Although Scott was in these days less switched off than he had been formerly, there remained significant difficulties with verbal comprehension. His sentences were delayed, he was not sufficiently specific when using nouns and he had a few strong word preferences. His speech and language problems were discussed with his mother in terms of his personality traits and a sympathetic and generally nonintrusive approach was taken by her and by me to improve his listening. He watched and listened to me while I 'played' – at first almost silently, then talking quietly to myself. In this way he could attend with meaning to details such as colours, prepositions, adjectives, verb tenses, questions (not addressed to him), pronouns, comparatives, etc., and he became able to attend to sentences which contained more than one idea. He soon began to join in the activities of his own accord, since he could do so on his terms, and to seek attention. He even began to correct my actions and gave his own versions, verbally.

Whilst appropriate models of language were given to Scott by his mother and by me and his verbal expression was unobtrusively assisted, he was not criticised for his speech and language and any failure to listen and comprehend. His mother gave him careful, precise information and did all she could to allay his fears and respect routine. His involvement and confidence gradually grew so that he was not seriously hampered by difficulties when he later attended primary school. And happily, he did not develop any tics.

In the case of Louisa, an upfront approach suited:

Louisa

At five years of age Louisa displayed marked autistic traits and no speech other than one or two words but she progressed well, aided by a classroom assistant with whom she formed a close attachment. Although this particular lady took a jolly, upfront approach she was consistent and predictable, made use of repetition where Louisa enjoyed it, and was sensitive to her needs, knowing when to back off. At six, Louisa used a variety of words, albeit sparingly, and involved herself more in her surroundings. Her liking for order and classification was utilised by leaving her to tidy the classroom and this probably gave her a sense of purpose and peace of mind.

And Shiva benefited from both types of approach:

Shiva

Sometimes hankering after a 'remedy' is inappropriate. Even for those who are motivated to shed some autistic ways, increasing one's involvement in the world can be an extremely distressing experience. When someone is heavily programmed to behave in a particular way, it should not surprise us to find that, in attempting to change, steps are taken forwards and backwards. It is indeed a brave thing to confront new territories, intense emotions, fear and panic without resorting to former safe strategies or escape routes. The more gradual the process, the less painful it is likely to be.

Shiva is nine years old and suffers from a severe degree of autism. He spends his time engaged in sensory activities. He has never spoken. He attends to patterns and music but his rocking is not synchronised with the music. He rocks on his feet while he grinds his teeth and jerks his fingers. Sometimes he laughs with delight. Sometimes he sucks his thumb. Sometimes he scratches himself.

Shiva is aware of and relates to people in his own way. He likes their company if they silently join in his repetitive rocking – up to a point. He likes them to tap or stroke his arm and leg repetitively, but again, only to a degree. He might hand someone an object if it were requested quietly and he might guide somebody to carry out an action for him. Shiva trusts the person he knows he can control. He can cope with occasional matter-of-fact requests. He can enjoy being tapped or stroked if he knows that when he removes the hand which taps him, it will be kept away. He seems content for someone to rock with him as long as he knows the activity will be ended as soon as he turns away. He has recently begun to experiment more with sounds – but he does not like to hear this behaviour praised or to have a repeat performance requested. It will be appreciated that Shiva profits from a nonintrusive approach based on good observation of his reactions, which can be written down to aid one's thinking and measure progress. It is at those times in which he is relaxed in another's company, that he can cope with a small request delivered in a noninvasive manner.

Shiva's advances are small and he only makes them when he feels sufficiently relaxed; nevertheless they are real. Training people with autism out of experiencing other people as sensory phenomena, through their smelling and touching of them, etc., may make them more socially acceptable but might leave them bereft of feeling. This is obviously a different kind of 'advance' and illustrates the importance of understanding.

Although Shiva benefits from a nonintrusive approach, he is learning from an upfront one which is going on in parallel. He has known his teachers for some years and they behave consistently in the classroom where there is plenty of repetition, structure and routine. Although he is not involving himself in general classroom activities there is evidence that he is taking some notice of them. Within a framework of familiarity and some predictability, he can venture to learn some ways of the world and even enjoy another person's vivacity, from a distance.

Sometimes removing a cause of anxiety is all that is needed:

Joel

Joel had begun to repeat sounds, syllables and words regularly and he was at risk of developing a stammer. He was very sensitive to criticism, rather a worrier and told people to say things which he wanted to hear repeated. When his mother said that he did not get frightened, the little three-year-old strongly refuted the statement, saying that he did not like the dark and going upstairs on his own. After he had discussed his fears and concerns with his mother, and with her paying careful attention to them, acting on them and reassuring him, his dysfluency disappeared and had not returned a year later.

Ian

Ian, too, was a three-year-old who was at risk of developing a stammer. He had already begun to have the occasional struggle to get out a word. He attended both a 'playgroup' and a 'playschool' and although he enjoyed going to both of them it did transpire that he had some worries about doing the right thing at his playschool where more was required of him. His mother took him away from the playschool and increased his time at the playgroup. His dysfluency disappeared.

Carl and Anton

These two unrelated adolescent boys each had many personality traits which suggested high levels of anxiety and both functioned in a somewhat shut-down state. Carl attended a mainstream school whilst Anton attended a unit for learning disabled youngsters. Carl was given compulsory homework along with the others in his class. It was the source of a great deal of distress for him and resulted in nightly tearful episodes. Anton was given plenty of choice regarding homework. He was permitted to take it or leave it and could decide its quantity too. The same arrangement applied to his classmates. He delighted in taking some home and enjoyed doing it. As will be appreciated, Anton and Carl were by no means identical in temperament or ability and indeed, Carl did show many more symptoms of overt anxiety. Further, his homework was of a significantly higher level of complexity than Anton's. Yet Carl might have fared better with some flexibility regarding his homework. His anxiety levels were certainly aggravated by the arrangement offered him. Giving him concessions may have had some negative effects – socially, for instance – but these might have been more than offset by decreased anxiety over the homework. The maximum possible reduction in anxiety might be our best yardstick, since lessened anxiety should result in improved social responses and general learning.

Treatment based on understanding helped Jerome, Josie and Lydia to overcome their literacy problems:

Jerome

Jerome's reading age at the age of nine years and four months was six years and seven months. He suffered from eczema and asthma and throughout his eighth year had been sick in the morning before going to school. He was methodical and conscientious, insisting upon writing in his diary every day, although it often troubled him very much to think of something to say in it. He was poorly co-ordinated, left-handed, had sucked his fingers from birth and had problems organising himself, particularly with regard to time. He panicked easily and worried about his health. As a three-year-old he had shown great anxiety about night-time darkness and the fact that an uncle did not have a wife.

If asked to read aloud, Jerome began reasonably successfully, though too speedily, but his performance deteriorated as he continued. Eventually he would regain his powers, only to lose them again and fall into a temporary panic-filled silence in which his faculties were quite shut down. His spelling was likewise patchy for his ability to write a word was not necessarily related to its difficulty, but rather to his state of mind. There was no true pattern or consistency in his errors. He had regular help from an elderly lady with whom he had formed a close relationship. When he read and wrote with this lady his skills showed improvement but his problems returned to him at home and in the classroom.

Jerome was visibly relieved to learn that his difficulties resulted from habitual responses and to find that his feelings and experiences were understood and explicable. He was introduced to the spelling method described in Chapter Six and became more relaxed and confident when reading and writing. For some months he was not asked to read blocks of text aloud, which would have risked reinforcing his negative reactions and undermined new, positive ones. He had a good relationship with an understanding teacher and made excellent progress as positive experiences began to out-number the negative ones. No longer dominated by the problem, he gradually began to cope with his various classroom activities in a way he had never been able to before.

Josie

At the age of twelve Josie was still finding it difficult to express herself on paper and, to some degree, in speech. Essay writing was particularly arduous for her and the difficulties had become more apparent as she had grown older.

She had generally been a happy, contented child but she was very sensitive to criticism, had passed through a spell of bed-wetting and was an ardent thumb-sucker from birth. Her elder sister was quick thinking, demanding and the cause of a lot of correction and raised voices in the family. Her playschool teachers had been vivacious, highly articulate and loud in their enthusiasm throughout all activities. Josie's parents were professionals and there was not a toy in the house which had not been chosen for an educational purpose. Nursery rhymes were not sung merely for enjoyment; they were to be remembered. Josie began to switch off a little at playschool but had, at the same time, exacting standards for herself, feeling the need to achieve.

Josie did obtain good reports from school but it appears, in retrospect, that she did not feel confident in her academic abilities. Her mother wondered if, in giving her daughter a great deal of help and tuition at home, she had robbed her of a true sense of self-achievement. She had become dependent on the assistance and her parents had offered it freely before the child had thought for herself. But such help was not available in the classroom, when panic and feelings of inadequacy are likely to have been fostered. Whilst Josie's difficulties might have arisen without such environmental influences, they may have been aggravated by them, aggravated indeed by experiences which another child with different personality traits might have profited by.

The remedy involved helping Josie, initially, to construct a short paragraph plan for an essay and allowing her a maximum of ten minutes at a time to write a paragraph under her own steam. Her efforts were given praise where it was due and something positive to say was always found. No criticism was implied nor correction given. The time limit for each little task helped Josie to relax in the knowledge that perfection was not to be expected, and to focus her mind on a task which was neither daunting in size nor in need of great organisation. As her confidence grew over the weeks and months, so did her ability to express herself, both on paper and verbally.

Lydia

Six and a half-year-old Lydia had difficulty expressing herself clearly, often seeming to get in a muddle and sometimes using the wrong word – and she was somewhat unwilling to communicate. Although she made some grammatical errors they were not consistent; she was aware of, and also used, the correct versions. She was unable to read any words reliably. Her father described her as a worrier. She had passed through a stage of speaking dysfluently at the age of four – repeating sounds, syllables and words.

Lydia was helped with her reading and writing in accordance with the methods described in Chapter Six, utilising her school reading books (which belonged to a scheme). Within a few weeks her confidence had grown for her literacy skills developed. She became more communicative and gradually began to speak with greater ease of expression. Her parents were delighted and fortunately Lydia responded well to everyone's praise.

Sometimes repetitive streaks can be utilised to good effect:

Will

Although Will was six years old and had good hearing, he had never spoken. His behaviour was extremely difficult to manage. He frequently head-butted, kicked, pinched, scratched, hit or bit people. If he did not receive one of the reactions he was accustomed to obtaining, he would persist, making a predictable response more likely. This compulsive aspect of his personality was recognised and utilised to encourage speech. When he made a noise it was imitated by the adult so that almost immediately he began to vary and experiment with sounds, especially when the adult's reply was not quite identical to his own utterance. Although actual words were not made use of by Will or the adult (who deliberately avoided them), speech did gradually begin to develop in the ensuing months.

Ralph

This highly dependent eight-year-old from a large family attended a unit for learning disabled children. He had become accustomed to take an extremely passive role in the classroom and at home. He refused to participate in any group activity, avoided many demands, collected objects and spent his time in a generally switched off state – although he repetitively took advantage of opportunities to escape from a room. Ralph spoke in single words but seldom put them together, in spite of having the capability to do so. He could, however, enjoy one-to-one attention from an adult (especially if he were being entertained) and he had a fondness for repetition. His habit of speaking only in single words was successfully broken through the use of a turn-taking game with, for example, a ball. The ball is rolled or thrown to one's partner on hearing a command or request. The simple commands "Go!", "Catch!" and "Come!" become gradually lengthened – for example, "Catch it!", "Catch it now!", "Catch it now, please!"; alternatively "Send it!" might grow to "Send the ball to me please". The repetitive nature of the activity was enjoyed by Ralph, who never seemed to tire of it, and although he remained reticent, his sentences were more easily developed outside the context of the game.

Ingrained habits can mean prolonged daily practice:

Simon

Simon was an anxious ten-year-old with a lateral *s* and difficulty pronouncing words in spite of a basic ability to use all sounds in context. He did not like seeing objects moved out of place, walked on his toes, visibly switched off and suffered from fits and some dyslexia. He enjoyed receiving attention, attended successfully to the correction of his *s* and responded enthusiastically to the approach taken for dyspraxia in Chapter Four. Owing to the long-standing nature of his speech difficulties however, brief daily practice for them had to be maintained in order to supplant well-established habits – in the case of his pronunciation problems, for almost a year.

Nevertheless, if a child is highly motivated to change his speech, the task can seem a relatively effortless affair – even when habits have become well-ingrained.

Compulsion dominated Thomas's speech:

Thomas

I have referred to children who are inhibited by praise, which seems to pressurise them or makes them aware that they are breaking their rules. Many children of course thrive on praise and positively seek it. Thomas, however, actively sought reproof. It can perhaps be assumed that in needing to hear often heard, predictable speech, he found it easier to manipulate for reproof than for praise.

Thomas deliberately misbehaved or requested forbidden things, closely observing a person's reaction. If he did not hear and see the predictable responses, he pestered for them by repeating his behaviour or requests, or he supplied them himself when all else failed – "You can't have the pen because you'll get dirty?" Indeed, he sometimes could be seen talking to himself, reliving negative cause and effect type conversations.

Care was taken by those involved with Thomas to give one short, clear and firm response to his behaviour and not to repeat it. At other times every opportunity was taken to give him positive responses and praise. Although it would be wrong to say that he began to actively seek praise, he did gradually begin to moderate his behaviour and his speech became much less driven by compulsion.

An understanding of Jeanette's problems enabled her mother to co-operate with some inconvenient treatment.

Jeanette

This seven-year-old girl displayed persistent avoidance behaviour with superficial sociability and a poor sense of personal identity and pride. She was easily embarrassed and had a strong appreciation of beautiful things around her. She was adept at manipulating adults.

Despite ample ability, Jeanette was not co-operating well with teachers at school. In the clinic her co-operation was patchy and restricted, though the task itself did not threaten her in any way.

An appointment was arranged for the end of the day. Jeanette began her usual manipulative behaviour but this was ignored. She was pleasantly told that a certain task was to be completed before she left the room. Her mother and I quietly busied ourselves with our own activities during waiting periods, giving as little verbal response to her comments as possible and avoiding confrontation or indication of frustration. The eventual completion of the task was acknowledged without hearty praise, which might well have produced a negative effect. Further end of day appointments were made and Jeanette's co-operation greatly improved.

WHEN PROBLEMS HAVE BEEN LONG-LIVED...

Those of us who are professionals working with children may have caseloads and demands on our time which seem enormous, but time spent discussing personality traits is time well spent and can result in more efficiency. It is particularly important not to be in a hurry when discussing problems with parents of older youngsters who have had their difficulties for a long time. A parent who, over some years has come to attach more blame to a hearing loss for his child's condition than maybe he should have done, or who perhaps mistakenly ascribes all a youngster's problems to a chemical imbalance or brain injury, for example, may well not take kindly to having his conceptions undermined. And certainly he will not want to be left with the impression that everything he has done in the past for his child may have been wrong – which is sure to be untrue, anyway. Obviously one needs to feel one's way very carefully indeed. If we are to be at all helpful, we must be sensitive.

AND WHEN PROBLEMS ARE NOT ACKNOWLEDGED...

It is also problematic when a parent seems quite blinded to his child's difficulties (possibly having chosen not to acknowledge them). He may appear unaware of the severity of the problems – perhaps reassured by the youngster's knowledge of, for instance, the first few letters of the alphabet. No matter that the ritualistic three or four-year-old is walking around in an automated state if he can demonstrate an ability to write A, B, C and D, count to ten and name some objects – everything else will come right at school.

REALISTIC CAREERS

When teenagers have mild to moderate difficulties socialising and em-pathising with others, there is a tendency to expect that all will be remedied with practice and maturity and they may be encouraged to take jobs which expose and highlight their lack of social skills. This can result in a string of confidence-sapping sackings. It is far better to have acknowledged that, however slight the problem may be, if the youth has always had it, it is unlikely suddenly to disappear. A position in a nursing home might necessi-tate brief, cheerful conversations, but perhaps not the social finesse required of a hairdresser, who is often called on to listen to and sympathise with clients' complex, worldly problems. No matter how artistic such a youth is, or how talented he is in some other area, if an important prerequisite for a job is to have good social skills, it is not for him if he is to be happy. Proper consideration of the matter may prevent unrealistic expectations and much misery. It might result in the youth's skills and attributes being well utilised in a working environment where people are understanding, appreciative and sympathetic.

CHAPTER ELEVEN

RESEARCH AND CONCLUDING THOUGHTS

My clinical enquiries and observations lead me to conclude that many speech and language disorders, dyslexia, autism, Asperger syndrome, Attention Deficit Hyperactivity Disorder and Tourette syndrome do not exist as entities which are independent of other conditions. Rather, they appear to result from an exaggerated manifestation of normal personality traits which overlap haphazardly throughout the various conditions – traits which can be associated with tension or anxiety. A child's diagnosis depends on which particular trait or traits dominate in his particular case. We have seen that switching off or a state of shutdown could result in the two quite different disorders, dyslexia and autism. We can acknowledge that problematic conditions, including Obsessive-Compulsive Disorder, are not uncommonly met in less severe forms. And we see strategies created by anxiety, causing further anxiety.

It is interesting to speculate that since males evolved as hunters and fighters they have needed to be more aggressive than females. Perhaps we have here a reason for the extra tension they appear to possess.

RESEARCH AND RATIOS

What makes a child manifest a specific trait or a specific group of traits? Moreover, if anxiety leads to traits, what might its level or nature need to be to result in an infant shutting out the world or part of it? We do not know the answers to such questions, but once we take a wider view of learning difficulties and mental illness, many specific research projects will have more meaning for us than they have at the present time; we should be able to relate them to one another more easily.

There appears to be a genetic predisposition towards developmental difficulties and mental illness and it may well be that this is associated with genetic predisposition to anxiety levels and types (assuming, of course, the broad definition of anxiety given in Chapter Two). Already a study headed by David and Brenda Comings (1991) is supportive of common genetic mechanisms. It suggests that a certain modifying gene is found more frequently in patients with Tourette syndrome, Attention Deficit Hyperactivity Disorder, autism and alcoholism.

The constancy of the ratio of males to females given for the following conditions is likewise suggestive of common causal factors of some kind:

RATIOS GIVEN BY SOCIETIES AND SUPPORT GROUPS

	Male : Female
Stammering	3–4 : 1
Other speech and language difficulties	3 : 1
Tourette syndrome	3–4 : 1
Autism (Asperger syndrome not included)	4 : 1
Asperger syndrome	6–10 : 1
Hyperactivity/A.D.H.D.	3–4 : 1
Dyslexia	3–4 : 1
Dyspraxia	4 : 1

In the case of mental illness, with its generally later onset, the ratios are less clear. The incidence of depression is approximately twice as high in women as in men but suicide is three times as common in men as in women, with young men being particularly at risk. It is widely accepted that women are more likely than men to seek help for stress and depression. Environmental factors complicate the issue and may affect or distort the figures.

According to Gwynneth Hemmings (1989), of the Schizophrenia Association of Great Britain, men seem to suffer an earlier onset of schizophrenia and suffer from it more severely, although in terms of numbers, as with manic-depressive illness, men and women appear to be affected equally. The current ratio of males to females who are suffering from schizophrenia and are being helped by the National Schizophrenia Fellowship's Office and Life Skills Project in London at the time of writing is 3.5 men to every woman. The significance of this ratio is unclear, however, since there is the possibility that men are more likely to be referred to the project.

The future may confirm an association between anxiety and a variety of syndromes and physical abnormalities. Working from their rheumatology clinic in Barcelona, Bulbena et al. (1993) have made a study of the association between joint hypermobility syndrome (JHS) and anxiety disorders. They found a high prevalence of anxiety disorders, in particular panic and phobias, among JHS cases. The strong association between panic anxiety and JHS was thought to provide a new basis for further studies on the genetic background of panic anxiety.

Evidence from a British twin study by Bailey and his colleagues (Bailey, 1995) suggests that multiple genetic influences may give rise to a phenotype considerably broader than autism as traditionally diagnosed. It also suggests that autism is a very strongly genetic neuropsychiatric disorder and that obstetric hazards usually appear to be consequences of genetically influenced abnormal development, rather than independent causal factors. The researchers identified biological hazards among genetically identical and fraternal twins where only one of each pair had autism (multiple congenital anomalies, neonatal convulsions, respiratory distress syndrome with and without cardiac arrest, delayed second birth, lower birth weight and haemolytic disease with and without arrested breathing). Any such hazard usually affected the individual with autism. Many of these individuals were affected by anomalies which occurred early in gestation (for example, minor congenital ones), which suggests that some aspects of abnormal development sometimes associated with autism are in existence early in the life of the fetus. If anxiety is associated with or a by-product of some genetic influence and responsible for some behavioural aspects of autism, and if it were to be experienced by a fetus, perhaps it might influence development before birth, just as it may do afterwards, and contribute to hazards such as neonatal convulsions.

Research studies suggest that a fetus can respond to music, differentiate between different kinds of music, and remember it, during the last three months of intrauterine life (Woodward and Guidozzi, 1992) and it is now believed that personality traits are exhibited in the womb. A.W. Liley points out that the pregnant uterus is a very noisy place where the fetus is active and responsive. He asks for consideration and respect to be accorded to fetal personality and behaviour (Liley, 1991). Fetuses display a variety of behaviour and it is well known that some suck their thumbs; this is possibly an early sign of some tension, although the importance to survival of a strong sucking action cannot be denied. Whether a fetus can feel pain, and at what stage in its development it might feel it, is the subject of much controversy (British Medical Journal debate: Do fetuses feel pain? 1996). Might not we also ask if and at what stage fetuses experience tension or anxiety, perhaps some to a greater degree than others? P.L. Righetti has been looking at the emotional state of the fetus in relation to that of its mother and concludes that the prenatal period is characterised by many emotional incidences (Righetti, 1996).

I have known five pairs of genetically identical twins with autism. The nature and degree of autistic symptoms in each twin and his co-twin have seemed similar, though not necessarily identical. It would be interesting to look at environmental effects more closely; they are, it appears, very significant in the later developing disorder, schizophrenia. In Tienari's study of identical twins (1963) there were sixteen pairs which each contained a member who suffered from schizophrenia. These contained no co-twin sufferers from the condition, although there were twelve co-twins with schizoid traits. Folstein and Rutter (1977) found that in four out of eleven identical twin pairs autism occurred in both individuals, with most of the remaining non-autistic co-twins showing some form of intellectual impairment, usually involving a speech or language deficit. When this sample was combined with a larger one in Bailey's more recent British twin study, the rate for both individuals of an identical pair having autism rose to 60 per cent and agreement for a social or intellectual disorder was 92 per cent. Genetic predispositions towards autism and schizophrenia certainly seem wide ranging in their manifestations. Further studies of identical twins could obviously be of great value in promoting our knowledge of personality traits, anxiety and all the various conditions we have been considering.

Could research into early personality traits increase our knowledge of epilepsy or allergies? Could it increase our understanding of why some children react more unfavourably than others to vaccinations? Could it add to our understanding of Sudden infant death syndrome? Could it improve our understanding of some other syndromes? Could it give insight into criminality? Could it help to explain why boys are more prone to problems than girls and why they are often in the shadow of girls of their own age? Could it...? Let us observe and be free with our hypotheses.

APPARENT CONTRADICTIONS

Many of the traits which might often be attributable to tension and anxiety can seem to contradict one another. One child, for example, may refuse to ask questions, whilst another may feel an unrelenting need to know and understand things. Again, one youngster may eat very little, another a great deal, or one tense or anxious person may become laid back whereas another may be active and industrious. Similarly, the child might be very dependent or independent.

The opposing characteristics are indeed numerous. Sometimes a single child will have symptoms which seem opposite to each other. He may, for example, show great fear in some situations and no sense of danger at other times, or have a very good memory for some things and a very poor one for others. There is, too, the youngster who develops covering up or coping strategies which lead one to believe that he is not at all anxious. In particular a great effort may be made to hide fear. Some young people seem to compensate for feelings of inadequacy by adopting social graces more appropriate to adult behaviour. Others appear more street-wise than they really are. A further factor which can bring confusion is a child's maturation. He may not appear anxious yet have adverse learning patterns which were laid down at an earlier date when he was more affected by tension.

It is conceivable that confusion might also originate from a possible tendency of the body to respond to an extreme reaction by initiating another extreme reaction in the opposite direction. Hence we have withdrawal (including depression), mixed with hypersensitivities, allergies, agitation, panic attacks and mania. If this idea has validity, and if there is, as there seems to be, a connection between anxiety and switching off, one might ask whether tension or anxiety leads to switching off or an early inclination towards switching off might lead to anxiety!

ON THE PLUS SIDE

Perhaps problems should not necessarily be seen as totally negative. There is no doubt that autism, hyperactivity and manic-depressive illness are sometimes conducive to great achievement in a particular area. Kay Redfield Jamison (1996) highlights this point with regard to manic-depressive illness, drawing attention to successful visual artists, writers and poets who were sufferers – including Byron who as a child displayed a violent temper, was venturous and fearless to a remarkable degree, and could be sullenly passionate.

In a biography of Florence Nightingale, Cecil Woodham-Smith describes Florence's behaviour and feelings as a young child. Whilst she was not naughty, she was considered strange, passionate, obstinate and miserable. She had an obsession that she was not like other people and avoided strangers to the point where she "worked herself into an agony at the prospect of seeing a new face, and to be looked at was torture." Doubting her own capacity to behave like others, she refused to dine downstairs. She escaped into dreams for hours at a time, a habit which she fought throughout much of her life because she had a great sense of moral duty. She fell into 'trance-like' states in the midst of ordinary life and often gave in to them *"with the shameful ecstasy of the drugtaker."* The behaviour became uncontrollable, hours at a time were blotted out and she lost sense of time and place against her will. At stressful times she moved like an automaton, unable to remember what had been said or where she had been. Her mind became blank and she looked at people vaguely, not knowing what they said to her. At the age of sixteen she had heard a voice which she believed to be that of God calling her to do good deeds; during her life her voices spoke to her on four occasions. She was prone to depression and self-condemnation. But her strong desire for a sense of purpose, her single-mindedness, her preciseness, her liking for detail and order, her passion for and great need to make lists and tabulate and absorb facts and figures and her phenomenal memory led her to perform an amazing service to mankind.

In some cases it might be construed that society is at fault for not being able to properly accommodate a person. Just as Florence Nightingale had suffered severely when it was insisted that she stayed at home and behaved like a young lady of leisure, the child with an attention deficit and hyperactivity problem, for example, might not be best served by being made to sit still in a classroom for forty minutes writing about something which has failed to capture his interest.

In her book, *Through the Eyes of Aliens*, mute autistic savant Jasmine Lee O'Neill (1999) explains how she delights in her autism with its sensory experiences and special qualities. She challenges those without autism to understand, respect and value autistic behaviour rather than discriminate against its differences and try to change it. We might all do well to heed O'Neill's live-and-let-live policy and ensure that the help we offer the person with autism is not found to be interfering and disturbing.

AND SO...

It is indeed better to try to understand the individual rather than a problem or condition he may have, for if there is an understanding of the person there is also an understanding of his difficulties. When a child's personality is understood through the use of a checklist and holistic approach, there is generally some relief for his parents. With comprehension comes tolerance and an improved sense of purpose or direction, and everybody benefits. Conversely, resigning oneself to the idea that a child has a specific condition or syndrome can be limiting.

With a better understanding of a child's personality and with being better in tune with his feelings there comes an improved understanding of test results and hence they become more useful. We are more likely to know when to test and when to restrict the testing because we are encouraging negative behaviour in the process. We might discover that we obtained results A when the child was engaging his brain and results B when he was not. We might notice at exactly what point a child's brain switches off.

Unfortunately the word anxiety tends to have rather serious connotations. Parents are unlikely to be pleased to be told that their children may be suffering from anxiety when there are no overt signs of it. When, however, they understand and link up the personality traits of their offspring they have no difficulty in seeing that the youngsters may have slightly raised, though normal, levels of tension, 'nervous energy', seriousness, anxiety, or sensitivity.

I have, in effect, tested the hypotheses laid down in this book in clinics and specialised schools and assessment centres in various counties of

England. When a child has difficulties it is generally the case that a certain measure of personality traits which can be related to anxiety or tension accompanies them, and existed prior to them. It is only through an understanding of these traits that we shall arrive at an understanding of the problems. We have many pieces of a huge jigsaw. It is time to be putting them together.

PERSONALITY CHECKLIST

Brain damage, genetic variations, and abnormalities in a person's anatomy or physiology can obviously have in their wake behavioural manifestations which may or may not be influenced by tension or anxiety. The purpose of this checklist is to consider the possible influences of tension or anxiety, whatever its cause and whether primary or secondary.

The questions which follow might interest us when considering a child's welfare. With the help of such questions and the reasoning laid down in this book, we can link aspects of the child's behaviour and so have an improved understanding of him. Since the interpretation of the answers to the questions is often affected by the manner in which they combine in each individual's case, I offer no scores or possible or probable diagnoses along the way; these might only serve to contain and restrict thinking. Our aim is to form a comprehensive picture of the child and to establish the manifestation and degree of his tension or anxiety rather than to label him narrowly. Relevant questions may be asked in the present or past tense, depending on which is the more appropriate.

Whilst some cases will necessitate a greater depth of enquiry than others, it is wise for a professional to allocate a generous amount of time to all initial appointments. In my experience, it is always required and is certainly cost-effective.

Professionals are also advised to avoid, in general, such all-encompassing questions as *"Is your son anxious?"* or *"Is he compulsive?"* For many people the words anxious and compulsive imply a degree of severity which we would not intend. We would risk alarming parents, receiving a negative reply and discovering nothing.

1. Does he have extreme temper tantrums?

    Does he overreact?

    Does he get really upset over trivial things?

    Does he have a 'short fuse'?

    Is he very determined or stubborn?

    Does he often seem miserable for no apparent reason?

2. Does he flit from one activity to another and have difficulty sustaining his interest in, for example, a toy?

    Can he sit still and concentrate?

Can he concentrate when he is really interested in something? If so, how well?

Is he impulsive?

Does he fiddle with ornaments, etc., in people's houses or with things in shops, despite being told not to?

Does he always seem to be restless and does he keep fidgeting?

Is he always in a hurry to do things?

Does he become bored easily?

Does he become very excited?

Is he easily distracted?

Is he very impatient?

Does he look where he is going – is he properly aware of obstacles in his way?

Does he awaken distraught after a daytime nap?

3. Is he easily frightened?

    Does he become terrified of anything?

    Is he anxious in an unfamiliar place?

    Does he worry?

    Does he panic?

4. Does he sleep well?

    Does he want to sleep with his parents?

    Is he frightened of the dark?

    Does he mind being left on his own at night?

    Does he have nightmares?

    Does he sleepwalk?

    Does he wake up in the night or very early in the morning?

5. Is he sensitive and easily hurt by criticism?

    Does he sulk?

    Is he very shy?

    Is he weepy?

6. Does he wet the bed?

    Does he wet himself during the day?

Does he have loose bowels?

Does he soil himself?

Does he suffer from constipation?

Does he have a lot of stomachaches?

Did he, as a baby, suffer from 'colic'?

7.   Was he a very good baby?

Did he scream a lot or have, for example, a high-pitched squeal?

Does he like to be cuddled?

Is he aloof?

Does he use people rather like tools – leading them to do things for him?

Did he crawl?

Was he late with his 'milestones'?

8.   Is he clumsy (perhaps not in all ways)?

Does he fall over a lot or bump into things?

Is he accident prone (perhaps in spite of being agile)?

Does he have difficulty hopping?

Does he have difficulty catching and throwing a ball?

Does he put out his arms properly to save himself when he falls?

Did he crawl normally?

Does he hold onto things properly?

Is he floppy or does he seem to have poor muscular tone at times and perhaps use too much force at other times?

Does he walk heavily?

Does he grip a pencil properly or according to his age?

Is he ambidextrous or left-handed?

Was he slow to establish a hand preference?

Does he dribble?

9.   Does he bite himself, bang his head, pull out his hair or hurt himself in any other way?

Does he respond to pain?

Does he respond to temperature?

10. Does he have a sense of danger appropriate for his age?

    Does he wander off?

    Might he go off with anyone?

11. Can he dress himself?

    Is he very slow at dressing?

12. Does he suck his thumb or a dummy?

    Does he bite his nails or chew his fingers?

    Does he suck a rag or his sleeve?

    Is there something from which he will not be parted?

    Does he rock himself?

    Does he grind his teeth?

13. Is he fussy?

    Does he mind getting dirty?

    Is he very orderly?

14. Is he a fussy eater?

    Is he particular about the texture of his food?

    Does he eat very large quantities of food or eat greedily?

    Does he eat or drink very little?

    Does he get hungry or thirsty?

    Does he keep wanting to eat the same things?

15. Is he upset by small changes to familiar things around him (yet perhaps happy to move house or go on holiday)?

    Does he insist on having, for example, the same brand of biscuits?

    Will he only eat in certain places or seem too embarrassed to eat in front of others?

    Will he only go to the toilet in certain places?

    Does he long to be home in his own bed after a holiday?

    Does he like to wear the same clothes?

    Would he wear a warm coat in hot weather?

    Does he like to take the same route?

Does he mind his mother helping at playgroup if she is not normally there?

Does he have any rituals?

Does the day tend to be organised around him and his needs?

Does he tend to walk around carrying things?

Is he very possessive?

Does he collect things, such as labels or rubbish?

Does he have any obsessions, e.g., for cars, trains or lawn mowers?

Does he flap his hands, spin objects or carry out some other action repetitively?

Does he like to watch the same video over and over again and object strongly if any part is missed out owing to fast-forwarding?

Does he have vocal mannerisms, such as a repetitive cough or utterance?

Does he keep sniffing, jumping, blinking his eyes or moving them in an unusual way or does he have any other kind of tic?

Do you find that he keeps making you repeat your own behaviour – perhaps by being defiant?

16. Does he have his own way of walking?

    Does he waddle?

    Does he walk stiffly?

    Does he walk or run on his toes?

17. Does he have, or has he ever had, a convulsion or epilepsy?

18. Does he suffer from allergies?

    Is he prone to recurrent ear, nose or throat troubles?

19. Has he ever regressed in his behaviour?

20. Does he seem aggressive or spiteful?

    Does he respond to punishment?

    Is he defiant?

21. Does he talk?

    Was he late to begin to talk?

Did he start to speak and then stop speaking?

Does he ever refuse to talk?

Does he mumble?

Does his speech sound like gibberish, or a language of his own?

Do you think that he could talk or could talk clearly if he wanted to?

Does he assume a silly or odd voice or use inappropriate intonation?

Does he seem to attend to the patterns of speech rather than to its meaning?

Is his speech factual and lacking in emotional content?

Does he have a hoarse voice?

Has he ever said a word once and then refused to say it again?

Has he ever pronounced a word clearly once and then refused to do it again?

Does he seem to retain his own words for things or his own pronunciation of words?

Does he retain *me* for *I* or refer to himself by his name, *he* or *you*?

Does he use *he* for *she* or confuse *he* and *him* (or other pronouns)?

Does he refuse to use certain words?

Does he seem to name objects inaccurately?

Does he often seem to choose the wrong word?

Are his sentences immature?

Is his speech repetitive?

Does he repeat what you say back to you or echo back something else he has heard?

Does he want you to repeat the same thing in exactly the same way?

Does he ask questions?

Does he seem to use questions as statements, or vice versa?

Does he keep asking the same questions?

Does he answer questions?

Can you hold a proper two-way conversation with him?

Does he talk at you rather than with you?

Is he difficult to keep on track?

Do his sentences seem muddled or back to front?

Is he dysfluent – does he repeat syllables or struggle to get out his words?

Does he rush and clutter his speech?

Are his breathing patterns disturbed when he talks?

Does he seem to have difficulty pronouncing some words in spite of being able to pronounce all the sounds correctly in their various positions and combinations?

22. Is he slow to understand? Do you have to explain something in two or three different ways or give very clear, precise instructions before he understands?

    Does he insist upon receiving very detailed explanations?

    Does he want definite statements and become distressed when something *might* happen or when things are in doubt?

    Does he seem to have difficulty understanding time sequences – understanding words like *yesterday* and *tomorrow*?

    Does he take what you say literally and seem unable to be flexible in his thinking?

    Does he misinterpret pictures?

23. Does he listen well?

    Does he listen well when he is being addressed in a group?

    Does he switch off or seem switched off from his surroundings – perhaps appearing deaf without being deaf?

    Does he remember nursery rhymes?

24. Does he understand gestures and facial expressions and use them appropriately?

    Does he seem to laugh inappropriately?

    Does he seem to have difficulty judging what others are thinking or feeling?

    Does he seem not to be upset by sad events?

    Does he seem selfish or callous?

25. Does he pay more attention than is usual to extraneous sounds?

    Does he stare at or scrutinise his surroundings?

    Does he stare at or 'through' people?

Does he squint?

Do his eyes dart?

Does he exhibit poor eye contact with people?

Does he disregard pictures or stare at them intently?

Does he close his eyes when he hears a noise?

Does he seem to need to feel things a lot?

Does he smell things a lot?

26. Does he play imaginatively?

    Does he keep playing with the same things?

    Does he line up cars but not play with them?

    Does he play well with other children?

    Does he seem egocentric?

27. Does he seem very dependent?

    Does he seem very independent?

28. Does he avoid demands?

    Will he do things of his own accord but not when asked?

    Does he employ strategies and manipulate people in order to avoid demands – does he do any of the following things?

    divert someone's attention

    pretend to cry

    say "in a minute"

    make excuses – say he is tired, unwell or busy

    pretend not to be able to do something

    flatly refuse to do something

    behave in a disruptive manner

    act in a silly way or giggle

    manipulate people by charming them

    say something is boring or silly

    say "I don't know"

    waste time

    ignore the speaker

keep up a frantic pace of activity

talk very quickly to prevent a person speaking

talk to a person non-stop, perhaps talking nonsense, to avoid being spoken to.

29. Does he seem to lack motivation?

Does he respond well to praise?

30. Does he have an extraordinarily good memory for past events?

Has he an extraordinarily good visual memory (perhaps for drawing)?

Has he an extraordinarily good auditory memory (perhaps for music)?

Is he able to repeat large chunks of information to which he has been listening?

Is he unusually good at certain activities or does he have any extraordinary skills?

EXTRA QUESTIONS WITH PARTICULAR REFERENCE TO THE CHILD OF SCHOOL AGE

Is he failing at school?

Does he have difficulty absorbing information?

Does he seem unable to commit information to memory?

Does he seem to have difficulty retrieving information?

Does he have difficulty following instructions?

Does he have difficulty organising his work, writing essays, etc.? Does he not seem to know where or how to begin?

Does he have difficulty making decisions or choices?

Can he read well?

Can he spell well?

Does he write letters round the wrong way?

Does he write very slowly?

Does he rush his work and not pay attention to detail?

Does he often repeat or omit words when he writes?

Does he press too hard on his pencil?

Is his work untidy?

Does he run his written words into one another?

Does he understand what he reads?

Can he be specific when answering questions?

Is he generally disorganised?

Does he keep losing things?

Do his possessions become very tatty or messy?

Does he show any signs of lacking confidence and self-esteem?

Is he very methodical?

Is he a perfectionist?

Does he seem 'laid-back'?

Is he pessimistic?

Is he irritable?

Does he get very angry?

Does he become very tired and seem lethargic?

Does he seem apathetic?

Does he try to evade school?

Is he disruptive?

Is he rude?

Is he defiant?

Might he start fights?

Is he accepted by other children?

Does he relate better to adults?

Does he show a sense of pride?

Does he seem oblivious of the impression he makes on his peers?

Does he lack inhibitions appropriate to his age?

Might he go 'over the top'?

Is he too familiar with teachers or strangers?

Does he imitate his teacher's speech?

Does he seem precocious?

Does he seem pedantic?

How well does he understand humour, irony and sarcasm?

Might he confuse play with reality?

Does he tell lies, without seeming to have a conscience and without appreciating the consequences?

Does he copy bad behaviour without seeming to understand its significance?

Might he do seemingly senseless, incomprehensible things?

REFERENCES

ADZHIMOLAEV, T.A., DOLETSKII, S.Y., AMINZHANOV, S.A., KORNIENKO, I.A., GOKHBLIT, I.I. & KUROCHKIN, Y.A., (1989). Effect of emotional stress on autonomic parameters in children and adolescents. *Human Physiology*, **15**, 256–262.

AGARWAL, K. & SETHI, J.P., (1978). A study of psychogenic factors in bronchial asthma. *Journal of Asthma Research*, **15**, 191–198.

ANGOLD, A., (1988). Childhood and adolescent depression II: research in clinical populations. *British Journal of Psychiatry*, **153**, 476–492.

ASPERGER, H., (1944). Die autistischen Psychopathen im Kindesalter. *Archiv für Psychiatrie und Nervenkrankheiten*, **117**, 76–136.

BAILEY, A., LE COUTEUR, A., GOTTESMAN, I., BOLTON, P., SIMONOFF, E., YUZDA, E. & RUTTER, M., (1995). Autism as a strongly genetic disorder: evidence from a British twin study. *Psychological Medicine*, **25**, 63–77.

BENSON, H., LEHMANN, J.W., MALHOTRA, M.S., GOLDMAN, R.F., HOPKINS, J. & EPSTEIN, M.D., (1982). Body temperature changes during the practice of g Tum-mo yoga. *Nature*, **295**, 234–236.

BLACK, P.H., (1994). 1.) Central nervous system-immune system interactions: psychoneuroendocrinology of stress and its immune consequences. *Antimicrobial Agents and Chemotherapy*, **38**, 1–6.

2.) Immune system-Central nervous system interactions: effect and immunomodulatory consequences of immune system mediators on the brain. *Ibid* 7–12.

BOURGEOIS, M. & ETCHEPARE, J.J., (1986). Les schizophrènes avant la schizophrénie. Enquête comparative et statistique sur les antécédents infantiles de 35 schizophrènes et de 35 sujets de contrôle. *Société Médico-Psychologique*, **144**, 757–766.

BRITISH MEDICAL JOURNAL DEBATE, (1996). Do fetuses feel pain? *British Medical Journal*, **313**, 795–798.

BULBENA, A., DURÓ, J.C., PORTA, M., MARTÍN-SANTOS, R., MATEO, A., MOLINA, L., VALLESCAR, R. & VALLEJO, J., (1993). Anxiety disorders in the Joint Hypermobility Syndrome. *Psychiatry Research*, **46**, 59–68.

COLERIDGE, S., (1875). Memoir and Letters of Sara Coleridge, ed. E. Coleridge (London: Henry S. King & Co.), p.20.

COMINGS, D.E., COMINGS, B.G. et al., (1991). The dopamine D2 receptor locus as a modifying gene in neuropsychiatric disorders. *Journal of the American Medical Association*, **266**, 1793–1800.

CORNISH, K.M. & MCMANUS, I.C., (1996). Hand preference and hand skill in children with autism. *Journal of Autism and Developmental Disorders*, **26**, 597–609.

CREEK, M. et al., (1961). Schizophrenic syndrome in children. *British Medical Journal*, **2**, 889–890.

DOUCHE, C., BARRAL, A., WINTER, R., DEZARD, X. & ZENATTI, C., (1990). Les strabismes secondaires à des troubles psychologiques. *Bulletin des Sociétés d'Ophtalmologie de France*, **90**, 59–61 and 64.

ETCHEPARE, J.J., & BOURGEOIS, M., (1986). Les antécédents infantiles des schizophrènes adultes II) Enquête anamnestique chez 35 adultes schizophrènes. *Société Médico-Psychologique,* **144**, 387–395.

FEIN, H., HUMES, M., KAPLIN, E., LUCCI, D. & WATERHOUSE, L., (1984). The question of left hemisphere dysfunction in infantile autism. *Psychological Bulletin*, **95**, 258–281.

FOLSTEIN, S. & RUTTER, M., (1977). Infantile autism: a genetic study of 21 twin pairs. *Journal of Child Psychology and Psychiatry*, **18**, 297–321.

GILLBERG, C., (1985). Asperger's syndrome and recurrent psychosis – a case study. *Journal of Autism and Developmental Disorders*, **15**, 389–397.

GRANT, I., (1985). The social environment and neurological disease. *Advances in Psychosomatic Medicine (Switzerland)*, **13**, 26–48.

GREENE, M.C.L., (1989). The Voice and its Disorders (London: Whurr).

HALLOWELL, E.M., & RATEY, J.J., (1996). Attention Deficit Disorder (London: Fourth Estate).

HEMMINGS, G., (1989). Inside Schizophrenia (London: Sidgwick & Jackson).

JAMISON, K. REDFIELD, (1996). Touched with Fire (New York: The Free Press, Simon & Schuster).

KANNER, L., (1943). Autistic disturbances of affective contact. *Nervous Child*, **2**, 217–250.

KUNZENDORF, R.G. & BUTLER, W., (1986). Personality and immunity: Depressive tendencies versus manic and schizophrenic tendencies. *Psychological Reports*, **59**, 622.

LANCMAN, M.E., ASCONAPÉ, J.J., GRAVES, S. & GIBSON, P.A., (1994). Psychogenic seizures in children: long-term analysis of 43 cases. *Journal of Child Neurology*, **9**, 404–407.

LILEY, A.W., (1991). The fetus as a personality. *Pre- and Perinatal Psychology*, **5**, 191–202.

MCMULLEN, T., (1991). The savant syndrome and extrasensory perception. *Psychological Reports*, **69**, 1004–1006.

MARSHALL, T., (1981). Life with Lowry (London: Hutchinson).

NEWSON, E., (1989). Pathological Demand Avoidance Syndrome: diagnostic criteria and relationship to autism and other developmental coding disorders. Pre-publication version, Child Development Research Unit, University of Nottingham.

NEWSON, E., (1996). Pathological Demand Avoidance Syndrome: a statistical update. Information Service, Early Years Diagnostic Centre, Nottinghamshire.

NORTH, C.S., (1988). Welcome, Silence (London: Simon & Schuster).

O'NEILL, J.L., (1999). Through the Eyes of Aliens (London: Jessica Kingsley).

ONSLOW, M., O'BRIAN, S. & HARRISON, E., (1997). The Lidcombe Programme of early stuttering intervention: methods and issues. *European Journal of Disorders of Communication*, **32**, 231–250.

PAULESU, E., FRITH, U., SNOWLING, M., GALLAGHER, A., MORTON, J., FRACKOWIAK, R.S.J. & FRITH, C.D., (1996). Is developmental dyslexia a disconnection syndrome? Evidence from PET scanning. *Brain*, **119**, 143–157.

RIGHETTI, P.L., (1996). The emotional experience of the fetus: a preliminary report. *Pre- and Perinatal Psychology*, **11**, 55–65.

SIMS, P.M., (1997). Some thoughts on stammering formed by a consideration of personality traits in young children. *Speaking Out*, **18**, No.3, Supplement on Children (The British Stammering Association).

SNYDER, A.W. & MITCHELL, D.J., (1999). Is integer arithmetic fundamental to mental processing?: The mind's secret arithmetic. *Proceedings of the Royal Society, B*, **266**, 587–592.

STEVENSON, J., GRAHAM, P., FREDMAN, G. & McLOUGHLIN, V., (1987). A twin study of genetic influences on reading and spelling ability and disability. *Journal of Child Psychology and Psychiatry*, **28**, 229–247.

TIENARI, P., (1963). Psychiatric illness in identical twins. *Acta Psychiatrica Scandinavica*, **39**, Supplementum 171.

TOTMAN, R., KIFF, J., REED, S.E. & CRAIG, J.W., (1980). Predicting experimental colds in volunteers from different measures of recent life stress. *Journal of Psychosomatic Research*, **24**, 155–163.

VAN REEMPTS, P.J., WOUTERS, A., DE COCK, W. & VAN ACKER, K.J., (1996). Clinical defence response to cold and noise in preterm neonates after intrauterine conditions associated with chronic stress. *American Journal of Perinatology*, **13**, 277–286.

WADHWA, P.D., SANDMAN, C.A., PORTO, M., DUNKEL-SCHETTER, C. & GARITE, T.J., (1993). The association between prenatal stress and infant birth weight and gestational age at birth: a prospective investigation. *American Journal of Obstetrics and Gynaecology*, **169**, 858–865.

WEINSTOCK, M., (1997). Does prenatal stress impair coping and regulation of hypothalamic-pituitary-adrenal axis? *Neuroscience and Biobehavioural Reviews*, **21**, 1–10.

WILLIAMS, D., (1998). Nobody Nowhere (London: Jessica Kingsley).

WILLIAMS, D., (1998). Somebody Somewhere (London: Jessica Kingsley).

WILLIAMS, D., (1996). Autism: An Inside-Out Approach (London: Jessica Kingsley).

WIMMER, H. & PERNER, J., (1983). Beliefs about beliefs: representation and constraining function of wrong beliefs in young children's understanding of deception. *Cognition*, **13**, 103–128.

WING, L., (1981). Asperger's syndrome: a clinical account. *Psychological Medicine*, **11**, 115–129.

WOLFF, S. & CHICK, J., (1980). Schizoid personality in childhood: a controlled follow-up study. *Psychological Medicine*, **10**, 85–100.

WOODHAM-SMITH, C., (1996). Florence Nightingale (London: Constable).

WOODWARD, S.C. & GUIDOZZI, F., (1992). Intrauterine rhythm and blues? *British Journal of Obstetrics and Gynaecology*, **99**, 787–790.

INDEX